MW00365169

Weaving China's Past

Weaving China's Past

The Amy S. Clague Collection of Chinese Textiles

Claudia Brown

with contributions by
Robert D. Mowry
Martha Winslow Grimm
Janet Baker
An-yi Pan

 PHOENIX ART MUSEUM

Design
  Mookesh Patel
  Alfred C. Sanft
    InfoDesign Management

Editor
  Anne Crowder Gully

Photography
  Marilyn Szabo

Additional photography courtesy of
  Moon Kim
    Center for Solid State Science
    Arizona State University
  Arthur Leeper
Lithography
  Orientations Magazine Limited
Printed in Hong Kong

Distributed by the
  University of Washington Press
  P.O. Box 50096
  Seattle
  Washington 98145-5096
  www.washington.edu/uwpress/

cover: number 5 [detail]
frontispiece: number 16
p. 14: number 23 [detail]
p. 22: number 1
p. 70: number 18 [detail]
p. 120: number 22 [detail]

Published by the
Phoenix Art Museum
1625 North Central Avenue
Phoenix, Arizona 85004-1685

Copyright 2000
Phoenix Art Museum
All rights reserved

Library of Congress
Cataloging-in-Publication Data
Brown, Claudia.
Weaving China's past:
the Amy S. Clague collection of
Chinese textiles / Claudia Brown;
with contributions by
Robert D. Mowry —— [et al.].

p. cm.

Catalog of an exhibition held at
the Phoenix Art Museum,
Feb. 19-June 10, 2000,
the El Paso Museum of Art,
Oct. 14-Dec. 30, 2001,
and the China House Gallery, China
Institute of America, New York,
Jan. 30-June 8, 2003.
Includes bibliographical references

ISBN 0-910407-39-8 (alk. paper)

1. Textile fabrics - China - Exhibitions.
2. Silk - China - Exhibitions.
3. Embroidery - China - Exhibitions.
4. Clague, Amy S. - Art collections
      - Exhibitions.
5. Textile fabrics - Private collections
      - Arizona - Phoenix - Exhibitions.
I.   Mowry, Robert D.
II. Phoenix Art Museum.
III. El Paso Museum of Art.
IV. China House Gallery.
V.   Title.

NK 8883.A1 B76 2000
746'.0951'07473 – dc21

Exhibition tour:
  Phoenix Art Museum
    19 February–10 June 2000
  El Paso Museum of Art
    14 October–30 December 2001
  China House Gallery
    China Institute in America
    New York
    30 January–8 June 2003

The exhibition is organized by
Phoenix Art Museum and
generously supported by:
  Ardie and Steve Evans
  The Asian Arts Council
    Phoenix Art Museum
  The Robert H. Clague Memorial Fund
    Phoenix Art Museum
  The Arizona Humanities Council
  Anne and Steve Thomas
  The Katherine K. Herberger College
    of Fine Arts
    Arizona State University
  Center for Asian Studies
    Arizona State University

Contents

In memory of Robert H. Clague

4

[Detail]

Foreword

Western admiration of China's silk textiles dates back at least to the days of the Roman empire, and for two millennia this admiration has remained undimmed. In the past century the establishment of the Chinese republic caused a large number of imperial costumes, no longer needed for court ritual, to enter collectors' hands and ultimately to travel to far flung regions. Many entered museum collections in North America. Textiles curators and conservators have studied these in depth, presenting occasional exhibitions of Chinese costume to the public. Yet American museums are just recently beginning to explore the broader topic of Chinese textiles, and to present splendid examples of the art along with porcelains, bronzes, enamels, and other decorative art traditions of China. In Arizona we are grateful to Amy S. Clague for enabling us to do just that here at the Phoenix Art Museum.

Amy Sanders Clague has assembled an extraordinary private collection of Chinese textiles of diverse styles, functions, and techniques. The collection is remarkable for its chronological expanse, with works ranging in date from the Song (960–1279) and Jin (1115–1234) dynasties through the Qing dynasty (1644–1911). One of the few private collections to include eighteenth and nineteenth century works together with early textiles, the Clague collection provides scholars and collectors a chance to examine trends over nearly a thousand years of development.

Born in El Paso, Texas, and educated at Smith College, Amy Clague has lived in Phoenix, Arizona for more than three decades. During that time, she has been involved with the Phoenix Art Museum, first as a volunteer in 1967, then as Development Director (1978–1982) and as a member of the Board of Trustees for the past seven years. She was a founding Board Member of the Museum's Asian Arts Council formed in 1985, and served as its President from 1986–88. She has been a friend throughout my twenty-five years here at the Museum. Throughout that time Amy has supported the Museum in collecting and exhibiting Asian art and acquired for her own collection contemporary crafts of both Asia and the West.

Amy Clague bought her first Chinese textile in 1989, a sixteenth century brocade altar frontal. Since then she has acquired more than thirty-five works, buying from dealers in London, Hong Kong, and New York. Her inspiration for collecting in a highly defined manner came from the accomplishments of Robert H. Clague, her late husband, who built three separate pioneering collections in Chinese art—the first in Chinese cloisonné enamels, the second in Chinese glass, and the third in Chinese bronzes. The cloisonné and the bronze collections are now permanently part of the Phoenix Art Museum collection, and the Chinese glass is now in the collection of the Hong Kong Museum of Art. In each case, the drawing together of a significant group of objects in one medium led to new discoveries in those fields and inspired further studies and exhibitions. The same is hoped for the area of Chinese textiles.

The first Clague exhibition, in 1980, coincided with the founding of the Phoenix Art Museum's Asian department and the appointment of its first curator of Asian Art, Claudia Brown. Now a professor of Art History at Arizona State University, Brown has been the primary organizer of the present exhibition, and continues with the museum as Research Curator for Asian Art. Recently joining the museum staff as Curator of Asian Art is Janet Baker, who has enthusiastically added her expertise to this project. The Museum has been pleased to have Robert D. Mowry, Alan J. Dworsky Curator of Chinese Art, Arthur M. Sackler Museum, Harvard University, as collaborating scholar on the project and as major contributor to the catalog. Martha Winslow Grimm, textiles conservator, undertook the technical analysis of the objects included in the catalog entries herein as well as the conservation of the objects themselves. An-yi Pan, briefly on the art history faculty at Arizona State University before moving on to Cornell University, contributed analysis and translations of the Imperial poems and other woven and embroidered texts.

More than most exhibitions, this project has involved the larger Arizona community. Radiocarbon dating of several works was carried out at the lab of Professor A.J.T. Jull at the University of Arizona in Tucson. Microscopic examination and analysis of selected textiles was performed by Dr. Moon Kim, of the Center for Solid State Science at Arizona State University. An interdisciplinary symposium on Chinese textiles was organized by the Museum's Asian Arts Council in collaboration with Arizona State University's College of Fine Arts and Center for Asian Studies, with funding provided in part by the Arizona Humanities Council. Offering a glimpse of the contemporary legacy of traditional textile arts, graduate students from the Fiber Arts Program of the School of Art, Arizona State University, opened their studios to symposium guests and participants.

The Museum gratefully acknowledges the many generous contributions to this project. Special thanks are due to Ardie and Steve Evans, without whose assistance the exhibition and catalog would not have been possible.

This catalog appears in conjunction with the premiere showing of the Amy S. Clague collection of Chinese textiles at the Phoenix Art Museum, as a part of *Three Chinese Traditions - Three Arizona Collections*, 19 February–10 June 2000. The three part exhibition included *The Gail and Stephen Rineberg Collection of Chinese Black- and Brown-glazed Ceramics, 400–1400* and *The Roy and Marilyn Papp Collection of Chinese Painting, 1400–1900* (recent acquisitions). All of these collectors deserve our thanks for allowing us to juxtapose works from their extraordinary collections to create an unusual glimpse of three unique traditions in Chinese art.

James K. Ballinger
The Sybil Harrington Director

Preface

Amy Clague's remarkable collection, incorporating superb examples from Song through Qing, allows art historians to re-assess the textile arts of China's recent centuries, 1100–1900. Textiles were often admired on a par with painting or calligraphy and could take inspiration directly from those fine arts. Their use in tribute and trade as well as in Buddhist ritual contexts is dramatically revealed in recent studies. The present study of works in the Clague collection explores these topics further and examines the relationship of these textiles to the greater fabric of Chinese art.

Amy Clague's collecting was stimulated by recent exhibitions of Chinese textiles in Hong Kong and New York. She lent several works to *Heaven's Embroidered Cloths: One Thousand Years of Chinese Textiles*, organized by the Hong Kong Museum of Art in 1995, the first major international exhibition to bring together textiles and costumes from collections throughout the world. The gathering of scholars and collectors at the symposium for that exhibition fueled her interests. She was inspired to continue collecting a broad range of styles and techniques within Chinese textiles and to seek works of varying function rather than concentrating on aspects of costume, an area where many significant studies have already emerged.

Two years later The Metropolitan Museum in New York and The Cleveland Museum of Art held a joint showing of Central Asian and Chinese textiles in the exhibition called *When Silk Was Gold*, and this gave further inspiration to Amy Clague's collecting. She resolved to follow the example of James C.Y. Watt and Anne E. Wardwell, who set a high standard of scholarship in their groundbreaking study of Chinese and Central Asian textiles. She thus has allowed her textiles to be subjected to technical analysis and radiocarbon dating as well as full examination by a textiles conservator. The results of these studies appear in the catalog entries below.

From the beginning of her collecting, Amy Clague has been keenly aware of the special conservation requirements of textiles. She has worked closely with textiles conservator, Martha Winslow Grimm, to adapt the conditions in her home for optimal control of light where textiles are displayed, and to provide protected storage conditions as well. To ensure that each piece is maintained in the best possible way, the conservator, working together with David Restad, Exhibition Designer, Phoenix Art Museum, has mounted many of them for display, using superior materials and techniques.

A detailed technical analysis of each piece in the collection has been carried out by textile conservator, Martha Grimm. She has identified the yarn type, thread count, and weave, and has analyzed the supplementary materials employed. She has also been involved in the photographic documentation of the works. Several of the brocades in the collection feature gold fibers, and these have been analyzed to identify specific techniques such as gold adhered to animal substrate, gold adhered to paper, or silk fibers wrapped with gold. Microscopic examination and analysis of these was performed by Dr. Moon Kim, of the Center for Solid State Science at Arizona State University.

A remarkable discovery was the use of peacock feathers twisted with silk fibers in a *kesi* woven during the Qing dynasty. Visiting scholar, Krishna Patel of the National Institute of Design, Ahmadabad, India, pointed out the use of the "barb" of the peacock feather, with remnants of the quill showing on the back of the textile. Confirmation was supplied by forensic ornithologist Beth Ann Sabo, at Wildlife Forensic Services in Irving, Texas.

Radiocarbon dating of several works was carried out at the lab of Professor A.J.T. Jull at the University of Arizona in Tucson. Ming dynasty dates for two Buddhist works in the collection were confirmed by this method, and earlier testing both at University of Arizona and at Oxford had established the dates of several other works. Such testing of silks is important for establishing the chronology of Chinese textiles, and it may have future implications for the authentication of the silk supports for painting and calligraphy.

With this technical data established, Robert D. Mowry, Alan J. Dworsky Curator of Chinese Art, Arthur M. Sackler Museum, Harvard University, has contributed his expertise to the preparation of this descriptive and analytical catalog. Dr. Janet Baker, Curator of Asian Art, Phoenix Art Museum, has contributed substantially to the catalog. Michael Komanecky, Chief Curator, Phoenix Art Museum, offered many helpful insights and suggestions. Lindsey Pedersen, Phoenix Art Museum Intern, skilfully edited the technical analysis sections of the catalog. Documentary photographs and close-up details were prepared by Marilyn Szabo. Translation of inscriptions has been contributed by scholars in diverse fields of study, including: Dr. An-yi Pan, Chinese art history, Cornell University; Dr. Anne Feldhaus, Religious Studies/South Asia, Arizona State University; Dr. Richard Salomon, University of Washington; and Jane Gregorie, Assistant Editor, Asian Arts online journal.

An extended catalog always involves many consultations with those knowledgeable in the field and an exhibition requires specialists in various aspects of exhibition design and preparation. A special thanks is extended to the following individuals who have contributed their expertise in various capacities:

Leesha Alston, Phoenix Art Museum
Janet Baker, Phoenix Art Museum
Terese Bartholomew, Asian Art Museum
Kathryn Blake, Phoenix Art Museum
Robin Burlingham
Jeana Burton, Phoenix Art Museum
Ju-hsi Chou, Cleveland Museum of Art
Christina Chu, Hong Kong Museum of Art
Carol Conover
Ardie and Steve Evans
Eugene Farrell, Senior Conservator, Harvard University Art Museums
Anne Feldhaus, Arizona State University
Bob Gates, Phoenix Art Museum

Dale Carolyn Gluckman, Los Angeles County Museum of Art
Jane Gregorie, Asian Arts online journal
Martha Winslow Grimm
Anne Crowder Gully
Chris Hall
Anthony J.T. Jull, The University of Arizona NSF-Arizona AMS Facility, Tucson
Moon Kim, Center for Solid State Science, Arizona State University
Elizabeth Knight, Orientations Magazine Limited
Gene Koeneman, Phoenix Art Museum
Michael Komanecky, Phoenix Art Museum
Paula Kornegay
Arthur Leeper
Professor and Mrs. Chu-tsing Li
Stephen MacKinnon, Arizona State University
Melissa Moy, Harvard University Art Museums
Heather Northway, Phoenix Art Museum
An-yi Pan, Cornell University
Krishna Patel, National Institute of Design, Ahmadabad, and Arizona State University
Mookesh Patel, Arizona State Unversity
Lindsey Pedersen, University of California, Santa Barbara
Brad Pochop, Phoenix Art Museum
Anna Ranero-Antolin, Arizona State University
David Restad, Phoenix Art Museum
Howard and Mary Ann Rogers
Beth Ann Sabo, Wildlife Forensic Services, Irving, Texas
Richard Salomon, University of Washington
Jacqueline Simcox
Rebecca Smith, Phoenix Art Museum
Milton Sonday, National Design Museum, Cooper-Hewitt, Smithsonian Institution
Michael Stevenson
Richard Stevenson
Jan Stuart, Freer Gallery of Art and Arthur M. Sackler Gallery, Smithsonian Institution
Marilyn Szabo
Allison Van Wyck, Phoenix Art Museum
John Vollmer
James C.Y. Watt, Metropolitan Museum of Art, New York
John Timothy Wixted, Arizona State University
Linda Wrigglesworth
Zo Choeje Rinpoche, Drepung Loseling Monastery

To further explore the historical and art-historical issues raised in this study, a symposium was held in Phoenix, 31 March–1 April 2000, organized jointly by Arizona State University and the Asian Arts Council of the Phoenix Art Museum, with additional funding provided by the Robert H. Clague Memorial Fund, the Arizona Humanities Council, and Anne and Steve Thomas. The following organizations and individuals contributed to the organization of the symposium or made scholarly presentations:

Asian Arts Council, Phoenix Art Museum
Arizona Humanities Council
College of Fine Arts, Arizona State University
Center for Asian Studies, Arizona State University
Janet Baker, Phoenix Art Museum
Frank Bell, Arizona State University
John Boppart
Deborah Boyer, Arizona State University
Francesca Bray, University of California, Santa Barbara
Ju-hsi Chou, Cleveland Museum of Art
Julie Codell, Arizona State University
Thomas Greives, Arizona State University
Karen C. Hodges, Phoenix Art Museum
Miyuki Imai, Arizona State University
Don and Jane Kauffman
Stephen MacKinnon, Arizona State University
An-yi Pan, Cornell University
Krishna Patel, National Institute of Design, Ahmadabad, and Arizona State University
Martha Raisanen, Arizona State University
Dan Shilling, Arizona Humanities Council
Laura Stone, Arizona Humanities Council
Nora Taylor, Arizona State University
Anne and Steve Thomas
Hoyt Tillman, Arizona State University
Yuko Umeda, Arizona State University
John Vollmer
James C.Y. Watt, Metropolitan Museum of Art, New York
Timothy Wong, Arizona State University
Paola Zamperini

Claudia Brown

Chronology

Shang	c.17th century B.C.–1028 B.C.
Zhou	1027–221 B.C.
Western Zhou	1027–771 B.C.
Eastern Zhou	771–221 B.C.
Spring and Autumn period	722–481 B.C.
Warring States period	481–221 B.C.
Qin	221–206 B.C.
Han	206 B.C.–A.D. 220
Western Han	206 B.C.–A.D. 9
Wang Mang interregnum	A.D. 9–23
Eastern Han	25–220
Six Dynasties period	220–589
Sui	581–618
Tang	618–907
Five Dynasties period	907–960
Liao kingdom	907–1125
Song	960–1279
Northern Song	960–1127
Southern Song	1127–1279
Xixia kingdom	1032–1227
Jin	1115–1234
Yuan	1279–1368
Ming	1368–1644

Hongwu reign	1368–1398	Chenghua reign	1465–1487
Jianwen reign	1399–1402	Hongzhi reign	1488–1505
Yongle reign	1403–1424	Zhengde reign	1506–1521
Hongxi reign	1425	Jiajing reign	1522–1566
Xuande reign	1426–1435	Longqing reign	1567–1572
Zhengtong reign	1436–1449	Wanli reign	1573–1620
Jingtai reign	1450–1457	Taichang reign	1620
Tianshun reign	1457–1464	Tianqi reign	1621–1627
		Chongzhen reign	1628–1644

Qing		**1644–1911**	
Shunzhi reign	1644–1661	Daoguang reign	1821–1850
Kangxi reign	1662–1722	Xianfeng reign	1851–1861
Yongzheng reign	1723–1735	Tongzhi reign	1862–1874
Qianlong reign	1736–1795	Guangxu reign	1875–1908
Jiaqing reign	1796–1820	Xuantong reign	1909–1911

The study of Chinese silk textiles, like the study of Chinese ceramics and metalwork, offers a glimpse into a complex tradition in which both organized industry and individual creativity played a role. Traditional China viewed spinning, weaving, and embroidery as divinely inspired arts to be practiced dutifully in the home.[1] Concurrently, however, luxury textiles were commissioned for religious, state, and private use. Silk was essential in China's foreign policy, used along with gifts of tea and silver to pacify borderlands.[2] Together with porcelain, silk became a major commodity for export to Europe. Elaborate techniques were developed for producing complex designs both in the woven cloth itself and in embellishments worked onto the surface. Brocades—fabrics woven with supplementary weft yarns to create complex patterns—were employed in many variations, including the complex lampas weave with its extra binding warps. *Kesi* ("carved silk"), a slit tapestry weave perhaps originally developed by Central Asians using wool yarns, came to be highly refined in the works of Chinese weavers of the Song dynasty (960–1279) and later. Embroidery, a means of embellishing a woven fabric with stitches made using a threaded needle, flourished throughout the history of silk textiles in China. Artistic experimentation in textiles increased at a level commensurate with that in ceramics and metalwork. As in those traditions, professional designers must often have worked out the compositions and decorative patterns for weavers and embroiderers to follow. At times during China's later dynasties, textile arts were pursued as fine arts,[3] appreciated on equal footing with painting and calligraphy.

The Study of Chinese Textiles

Until recently, much of the study of Chinese textiles revolved around Beijing's imperial palace—the Zijincheng, or Forbidden City—that became a focal point for interest in Chinese culture after the end of Qing-dynasty (1644–1911) rule in 1911. A fascination with court garments and regalia had already begun when Cixi, the Empress Dowager (1835–1908), sought to bolster foreign support for the government by granting interviews to foreigners.[4] In the years following the end of imperial rule and preceding the establishment of the Palace Museum within the former Forbidden City, many court costumes and other textiles were dispersed into collections worldwide. Stimulated by this direct contact and by the early publications of the Palace Museum, Western scholars took a keen interest in Chinese textiles as they came to know them through these court robes and interior furnishings.[5] This interest in palace costumes and decorations later expanded to included textiles preserved in the imperial art collections, and these came to be known through well illustrated volumes published in Taiwan and in China.[6] These publications provided a glimpse of textiles as art, sometimes for reproducing paintings or calligraphy but also as an art appreciated on its own.

A separate investigation of Chinese textiles was stimulated by stunning discoveries of well-preserved ancient textiles in Central Asian sites. Sir Aurel Stein's expeditions in inner Asia (in 1900, 1906–08, 1913–16, and 1930),[7] and particularly the discoveries at Dunhuang's Buddhist cave temples, yielded a new range of textiles for study, and brought about an early appreciation of the use of textiles in Buddhist contexts. Excavations in Siberia also contributed new knowledge of early Chinese textiles as fabrics made before the Han dynasty (206 B.C.–A.D. 220) were found in the Scythian tombs at Pazyryk (in 1929 and 1947–49).[8]

15

In the closing decades of the twentieth century, new approaches to the technical examination of Chinese textiles developed, just as, coincidentally, Chinese textiles that had been preserved in Tibet began to reach the world market. The latter, though lacking in specifics of provenance, have provided works of unprecedented age and quality for study and appreciation.[9] Technical studies emerged as conservators, conservation scientists, art historians, and textiles specialists worldwide turned their attention to China's broad range of weaving techniques,[10] particularly the distinctive *kesi* tapestry technique.[11] The flourishing Western interest in Buddhism promoted the study of textiles in the context of Buddhist ritual.[12] New studies of the economic history of China illuminated the importance of silk yarns and finished textiles in China's economy and in worldwide trade.[13] Meanwhile, Chinese textiles preserved in Japanese temples, including those preserved in the Shōsō-in—the imperial repository, dedicated in 756 at Tōdai-ji (the Great Eastern Temple), Nara, for the collection of Emperor Shōmu (701–756), which was donated at his death by his wife, Empress Kōmyō (701–760)—as well as various garments and other textiles believed to have been brought back to Japan by Buddhist monks returning from China have recently come under scholarly scrutiny, and traditional provenance records have been re-examined in light of other evidence.[14]

The effort to write a comprehensive history of Chinese textiles has recently begun, notably in the work of Chinese scholars[15] who have drawn from the above sources as well as from archaeological material. That this process has only now gained momentum is due to the surprising fact that until recently so few pre-Qing textiles were known that it would have been difficult to contemplate writing anything approaching a historical survey of the subject. Attention was concentrated on Qing court robes and rank badges, and a few fragmentary early pieces. The situation fundamentally changed, for just when an expanding quantity of old and often very well-preserved textiles—sometimes entire bolts of unused silk—began to flow out of Tibet and into the international art market, archaeology began to yield an abundance of early textiles. At the same time, art historians have recently pursued a deep interest in the technical study of works of art including bronze casting, ceramic production and other "minor arts." Happily, the field of Chinese textiles, through the efforts of collectors like Amy Clague, may soon leave the pool of neglected arenas of study.

The Archaeological Record
The wide-ranging uses of textiles have ensured their preservation in vast numbers of archaeological contexts. For China's early periods, such finds have confirmed the appearance of weaving in the fifth millenium B.C. and sericulture in the fourth millennium B.C.[16] These discoveries confirm the long standing belief that silk production first began in China and from there spread to other cultures. Finds in the Changsha region of Hunan province, including the spectacular tombs found at Mawangdui (c. 168 B.C.),[17] brought to light many textiles, including whole garments. These prove the development at least by the second century B.C. of complex techniques in weaving and embroidery as well as printed silk fabrics. For the later periods, a few archaeological discoveries stand out for their clear impact on our understanding of Chinese textiles: at Famensi (a Buddhist temple, near Xi'an, Shaanxi province), for example, the inclusion

in a ritual offering datable to A.D. 874 of miniature Buddhist vestments including a model of a *kasaya* (ceremonial mantle), an apron (or altar frontal), and clothing,[18] all couched with gold-wrapped threads on a silk gauze ground in patterns of lotus blossoms and clouds. Excavations of the foundations of Song dynasty pagodas have also yielded important documentary textiles,[19] just as tombs of the Song and Yuan (1279–1368) have provided important evidence. For the Ming period (1368–1644), few sites can surpass in significance for textiles the tomb of the Wanli emperor, in which cloth for imperial robes was well-preserved.[20]

Chinese Textiles in the Clague Collection

The Clague collection presents as its earliest work a silk brocade (number 1) associated with the Jin dynasty (1115–1234). The Jin dynasty was established by the Jurchen (Ruzhen) people who sacked the Northern Song capital of China in 1127 and captured the Song emperor Huizong. The Song court re-established itself in the south with a new capital at Hangzhou, while the Jin ruled the northern part of China. Thanks to recent scholarship,[21] a number of surviving textile fragments can be specifically associated with the Jin, who had been a semi-nomadic ethnic group in the borderlands of North China but now established fixed capitals in the Chinese heartland, first at Beijing (1153) and then at Kaifeng (1161). These works, together with slightly later brocades (number 2) dating to the Yuan dynasty (1279–1368), offer an opportunity to examine the complex and varying weave structures—and the ingenious inclusion of gilt wefts of leather or paper—employed by weavers for Jin royal patrons on the one hand and their Yuan successors on the other.

Scholars have recently noted the early development of regional styles and techniques in Chinese textiles. Centers for *kesi* production, for example, have been noted during the Northern Song period (960–1127) at Dingzhou, in Hebei province, and during the Southern Song at Hangzhou, in Zhejiang province,[22] then the imperial capital. Hangzhou also emerged as a center for needleloop embroidery,[23] a technique involving detached loops of silk yarns often backed with gilt paper (number 21). The same city was noted for meeting Tibetan commissions for woven Buddhist images. Hangzhou probably maintained this status throughout the Ming period, just as it remained an important center for painting. The Yongle reign (1403–1424) of the Ming dynasty saw a tremendous dedication of resources to the production of gifts, including textiles for Buddhist purposes; the practice carried over into the Xuande reign (1426–1435) as well (numbers 4, 6, 7).

Evidence of important stylistic changes and technical shifts can be noted in the seventeenth century. Anthropologists and historians have identified a shift in importance among China's women from weaving to embroidery.[24] Increasing specialization meant that finished yarn and finished cloth could be purchased routinely.[25] This spurred a rising interest in embroidery among the gentry class, and a related rise in the status of embroidery[26] to verge upon that of the fine arts of painting and calligraphy. A manual of embroidery designs compiled by scholar-calligrapher Shen Linqi (1602–1664)[27] sets out many themes and patterns that would inspire embroiderers for centuries to come. For example the theme of a hundred children playing, seen in a nineteenth-century example in the Clague collection (number 25), was presented by Shen in his volume.

Special weaves such as *kesi* also became popular among late Ming scholars, especially those taking inspiration from woodblock-printed books (numbers 14 and 15). These textiles often represent themes of particular importance to scholars, emphasizing accomplishment, learning, and the study of antiquity. The exquisite choices and combinations of flora may reflect contemporary developments in the art of flower arrangement.

Foreign trade during the Ming dynasty made an impact on the textile arts. Documents record the inclusion of Chinese silk textiles along with porcelains in the earliest voyages of the Manila galleons in 1573. According to the inventory of Antonio de Morga (1559–1636), president of the *audiencia* at Manila, Spanish traders bought:

> raw silk in bundles, of the fineness of two strands, and other silk of coarse quality; fine untwisted silk, white and of all colors, wound in small skeins; quantities of velvets, some plain and some embroidered in all sorts of figures, colors and fashions, others with body of gold and embroidered with gold; woven stuffs and brocades, of gold and silver upon silk of various colors and patterns; quantities of gold and silver thread in skeins; damasks, satins, taffetas, and other cloths of all colors....[28]

It is interesting to find gold-wrapped threads sold in trade destined for Europe. These played an important role in Chinese textiles as well, as can be seen in the Clague collection in brocaded examples (numbers 8–10), *kesi* examples (numbers 12–15), and embroidered works (numbers 23–27).

By the eighteenth century, collectors viewed some textiles as the artistic equivalent of painting. The Qianlong emperor (r. 1736–1795), inspired by scholar-collectors of the late Ming as well as by the precedent of the Song Emperor Huizong (r. 1100–1125), commissioned scholar-officials to catalog his art collections (producing the *Bidian Zhulin* and the *Shiqu Baoji*, published in 1744–5, 1793, and 1816). These catalogs included examples of *kesi* and embroidery alongside painting and calligraphy. Court patronage for Chinese textiles is a complex and varied phenomenon. At the highest level of art and connoisseurship, the Qianlong emperor himself may have selected works to be "reproduced" in *kesi*, including his own painting and poetry (number 17) and works in his collection of painting and calligraphy (number 18).

Either directly or indirectly Qianlong and the other Qing emperors commissioned special textiles for interior furnishings. These can sometimes be identified with specific palaces, such as the tapestry probably woven for the Western style palaces of the Yuanmingyuan, in Beijing (number 16). Other textiles for palace use included desk frontals (number 22) and upholstery fabrics (number 24).

Highly visible in Qing imperial policies was the practice of using gifts of cloth, particularly cloth for dragon robes, as a means of incorporating the powerful leaders of vassal states into their own military bureaucracy. The Qing forebears had been on the receiving end of this practice during the late Ming. Silk had a long history in political gifts to peoples of the borderlands; Song examples are the most striking. Most visible among textiles surviving today are the lavish silk brocades bestowed upon Tibetan nobles and worked into garments (number 8) and furnishings (number 12).

Gifts within the court were important as well. Some of the textiles in the surviving palace collections appear to have been gifts from officials to the emperor.[29] Gift-giving was also important in a private context and this may have been one of the most enduring uses for textiles (number 27).[30]

One of the liveliest connections between the art of textiles and other Chinese arts is the link to painting and calligraphy.[31] This aspect of textiles flourished in privately commissioned works (numbers 14 and 15) and in imperial commissions (numbers 17 and 18). In the transition to modernity and the twentieth century, subject matter borrowed from painting and calligraphy remained an important inspiration for textiles (number 28).

Organization of the Catalog
The following catalog is organized around three major types of Chinese silk textiles: brocades, *kesi* (tapestries), and embroideries. Enlarged details appear on pages 27, 32, 34, 79, 85, 122, 126, 127, 128, 134, and the cover. For each entry a detailed technical analysis has been provided. Where available the results of radiocarbon dating—often called Carbon14 or C14 dating—are analyzed in light of other evidence. Photo-micrographic details are on pages 99 and 129. The detailed analysis of each work is offered with the intention of expanding the knowledge and appreciation of these highly refined works of art.

Claudia Brown

The author of each section is indicated:
[RDM]   Robert D. Mowry
[CB]   Claudia Brown
[MWG]   Martha Winslow Grimm
[JB]   Janet Baker

1 Recent studies (particularly Bray 1997) have explored the way in which the ancient homily, "Men till, women weave," played out in the lives of Chinese men and women over the later centuries of China's history.

2 On the extraordinary gifts of silk made by the Song court to border peoples—sometimes as much as 200,000 bolts at a time—see Rossabi in New York 1997, p. 10.

3 It is difficult to evaluate the authenticity of attributions to such famous weavers as Zhu Kerou (active 1127–1162) or Shen Zifan, or even the attributions to the Gu family of Shanghai or Ni Renji in Zhejiang. Future studies may identify specifically the contributions of these "names" in the history of Chinese textiles.

4 The Dowager Empress Cixi (1835–1908), whose influence on the arts at court was significant for nearly fifty years, allowed her portrait to be painted in 1903–4 by the American artist Katherine Carl. This and other accounts gave Westerners a glimpse of the rich decorative styles of the palace. A short time later the painter Hubert Vos (1855–1935) was commissioned to paint portraits of the Empress Dowager. One of these is now in the Fogg Art Museum, Harvard University (accession number 1943.162; Bequest of Grenville L. Winthrop).

5 For example, New York 1931 and New York 1945.

6 For example, National Palace Museum 1970, and Liaoning Provincial Museum 1982 and 1983.

7 Stein 1912, pp. 207–210, describes the textiles found in the "walled up temple library," at Dunhuang, including a large embroidery of a Buddha with bodhisattvas (pl. IX), an embroidered cushion cover with scrolling floral motifs (fig. 197), "a number of triangular head-pieces...detached from their painted banners...composed either in their body or in their broad borders of pieces of fine silk damask," and "a silk cover...intended for a manuscript roll." Stein speculated on the use of imagery from the Near East and Egypt in these textiles, but he concluded that they were most likely of Chinese manufacture. The objects collected by Stein are now in the British Museum and the Museum of Central Asian Antiquities in New Delhi, India. Another group of textiles was collected at Dunhuang by French archaeologist Paul Pelliot (1878–1945). These are preserved in the Musée Guimet and the Bibliothèque Nationale, Paris. See Riboud and Vial 1970. For a summary account of these expeditions, see London 1990, pp. 9–15.

8 Silk with woven patterns and silk with chain-stitch embroidery were found; Rudenko 1970, pp. 305–6 and pls. 134A and 178. Chinese silks were also found in Xiongnu (Scythian) remains at Noin-Ula.

9 A tendency to preserve and re-use fragments of silk textiles (numbers 8 and 12), perhaps inspired by the patchwork of the Buddhist priest's mantle (kasaya), is a distinctive aspect of these works.

10 In the forefront have been the Association pour l'Étude et la Documentation des Textiles d'Asie (AEDTA), Paris; The Cleveland Museum of Art; the Los Angeles County Museum of Art; The Metropolitan Museum of Art, New York; the Minneapolis Institute of Arts; the Royal Ontario Museum, Toronto; and the Victoria and Albert Museum, London.

11 For example, see Cammann 1948 and 1962.

12 For one of the most recent of these, see Gluckman 2000.

13 For example, Shih 1976 and Brook 1998.

14 For example, Zhao Feng 2000, p. 48, fig. 7.

15 For example, Huang 1985 and 1987, and Zhao Feng 1999.

16 Zhao Feng 1999, pp. 38–39.

17 See Hunan Provincial Museum 1973.

18 Zhao Feng 1999, pp. 306–307.

19 See, for example, Zhao Feng 1999, p. 210.

20 See Huang 1987, cat. nos. 31–38.

21 See New York 1997, Krahl 1997, and entry numbers 1 and 2 below.

22 New York 1997, pp. 58–59.

23 New York 1997, pp. 165–166.

24 Bray 1997, pp. 265–269; and Ko 1994, pp. 173–176.

25 For a recent discussion of this specialization in the production process, and of the growing importance of cotton production, see Brook 1998, pp. 194–198.

26 For examples of the "Gu family" style of embroidery, see Huang 1987, plates 63–66.

27 Illustrated and discussed in New York 1985, pp. 39–41.

28 See Shurz 1939, p. 73; and Brook 1998, p. 205.

29 Some inscribed textiles (for example, National Palace Museum 1970, cat. no. 32–33) bear inscriptions which parallel the wording on paintings or calligraphies presented to the emperor, and some include simulated seals reading "respectfully embroidered," a parallel to phrasing in signatures on court paintings and calligraphies.

30 Several recent studies have examined the role in Chinese art of gift giving. For example, see Clunas 1997–8.

31 Zhao Feng 1999, pp. 32–35, emphasizes the link between paper and silk, the use of silk grounds for painting and calligraphy, the use of painting to adorn costume, and the emergence of woven works of art.

Catalog

Numbers 1–10   Brocades

1 Rectangular Silk Panel with Phoenix-and-Cloud Medallions

Jin dynasty (1115–1234)
   Silk brocade; light blue silk ground of dyed yarns in tabby weave,
   the ground interwoven in brocade weave with flat strips of animal substrate
   faced with gold leaf
H. 96.5 cm and 99.0 cm; W. 64.5 cm, including selvages

This vertically oriented, rectangular silk panel sports six rows of rhythmically spaced, peach-, or teardrop-, shaped medallions brocaded in gold against a tightly woven ground of light blue silk. The staggered rows alternate in terms of number of medallions, including either four whole medallions, as in the bottom row, or three whole medallions and two half-medallions, as in the next row up, with the half-medallions appearing at the edges. Each medallion depicts a crested phoenix ascending majestically amidst clouds, its wings spread in flight, its tail trailing gracefully. Presented as if seen from above, each phoenix is arrayed with its head at the medallion's top, its feathered body and outstretched wings at the medallion's "shoulder", and its curving, segmented tail at the bottom; scrolling clouds flank each bird's body and tail, while small cloud wisps frame its head. The phoenixes alternate in orientation from row to row: in those rows with whole medallions only, the birds face the proper left and their tails trail to the proper right, creating S-curve compositions; in the mirror-image medallions in the alternating rows, the birds face the proper right and their tails flutter to the proper left, yielding reverse-S-curve compositions. The selvages along the left and right edges indicate that this panel preserves the full breadth of the original fabric; in addition, they reveal the width of the loom on which the fabric was woven, just as they unequivocally identify the orientation of warp and weft. Careful examination of individual threads, particularly those along the (recently cut) top and bottom edges and those concealed within the weave, reveals that the silk was originally light blue, the present turquoise hue resulting from slight fading.[1] The foundation weft threads, which are continuous from side to side, float across the backs of the brocaded areas to accommodate the gold-faced, supplementary wefts, thus preventing the finished fabric from puckering.[2] Those supplementary wefts are not metallic threads per se; rather they are wide, flat strips of animal substrate—probably sheep- or goat-hide leather—to which gold leaf has been applied.[3] Although the gold-faced, supplementary wefts are continuous within each medallion, they are discontinuous from medallion to medallion. Careful inspection of localized areas of wear—the second medallion from the right in the bottom row, for example—reveals that the damaged appearance is due more to loss of gold from the animal substrate than to soiling or to damage to the silk itself.

This panel is one from a small group of silk textiles—all said to have come from Tibet[4] and all with tightly woven, white or brightly colored monochrome, tabby-weave grounds embellished with patterns brocaded in gold threads[5]—that began to appear on the market in the mid–1980s. Though different from any Chinese textiles previously known, these fragments immediately were recognized on the basis of style as transitional between the patterned silks of the Tang dynasty (618–907) and those of the Yuan (1279–1368); their appearance not only occasioned great excitement but sparked considerable research, which led to the publication of several articles assigning the pieces to the non-Chinese Liao (907–1125) and Jin (1115–1234) kingdoms,[6] which bordered China on the north and which were roughly contemporaneous with China's Northern Song (960–1127) and Southern Song (1127–1279) periods respectively. The 1988 excavations of the 1162-dated tomb of Prince Qi, near Acheng, in Heilongjiang province, yielded garments fashioned of related fabrics: brightly colored silks with brocaded patterns woven with golden threads.[7] A member of the Jin imperial family—which was of non-Chinese, Jurchen stock—Prince Qi served for many years as the resident governor of Shangjing, the ancient Jin capital, which is near present-day Acheng.[8] That archaeological discovery, in concert with subsequent technical studies of weave structures, not only confirms the attribution of this group of silk textiles to the Jin dynasty but permits their association with Jin royal and aristocratic families.[9] Indeed, available evidence suggests that gold-brocaded silks were the most representative luxury textiles of the Jin dynasty.[10] Although the precise location of the textiles' manufacture cannot yet be determined, the weave structure and the use of animal substrate (rather than paper substrate) for the gold-faced supplementary wefts suggest that they were made in the Jin kingdom, rather than in China proper.[11]

In discussing a kindred panel of silk brocade in the collection of The Metropolitan Museum of Art, New York, James C.Y. Watt noted that "In the official history of the Jurchen empire (known by the dynastic name of Jin), which occupied northeastern China and central China as far as the Huai River, it is recorded that the material used for official robes was sometimes brocaded in gold."[12] Not only does this statement correlate precisely with the archaeological evidence, it marks an important point of contrast: although prized by the non-Chinese peoples to China's north, gold-brocaded silks seem to have found little favor with the Chinese them-selves, who, at least during the Song dynasty, tended to prefer less ostentatiously embellished fabrics.[13] Indeed, except for the occasional imperial portrait, in which an emperor might wear a robe emblazoned with golden medallions,[14] the Song painting tradition typically includes garments of gold-brocaded silk only when depicting wealthy "border peoples", to the extent even that the representation of such silks may serve as a signal that the wearer is of such ethnicity.[15]

Even if made in Jin territory for wealthy citizens of that state, the subject matter of this panel is purely Chinese in origin. By tradition, the phoenix, or *fenghuang*, appears in times of peace and prosperity. It numbers among the four divine creatures, or *siling*, mentioned in the Zhou-dynasty *Liji* [Book of Rites], along with the dragon, *qilin* (unicorn), and tortoise.[16] It presides over the heavens' southern quadrant and thus symbolizes the sun and warmth. Phoenix imagery had firmly established itself in the pictorial arts of the Warring States (481–221 B.C.) and Han (206 B.C.–A.D. 220) periods, the auspicious red bird appearing in the company of the green dragon, white tiger, and entwined black snake and tortoise which symbolize, respectively, east, west, and north.[17] A creature of good omen, the phoenix began to appear independently in the visual arts during the Six Dynasties period (220–589). Depictions from the Six Dynasties, Sui (581–618), and early Tang periods typically show the phoenix striding with legs

1
[Detail: front]

1
[Detail: back]

25

extended and wings outstretched;[18] from the late Tang and Five Dynasties (907–960) periods onward, however, the phoenix is usually shown in flight, its segmented tail flowing gracefully behind.[19] By the Northern Song, the bird was characteristically shown ascending, its head crested, its legs concealed, its tail segmented into five barbed filaments;[20] by the Southern Song, it was usually paired, either with another phoenix or with a *luan*, a mythical bird for which there is no English name.[21] Beginning in the Yuan dynasty the two different species of birds, the *luan* and the *fenghuang*, came to be viewed as two varieties of phoenixes distinguished only by their differing tails, the *luan* sporting a long tail segmented into five barbed strands and the *fenghuang* boasting a long, bifurcated tail whose curls recall scrolling tendrils.[22] By the Ming dynasty (1368–1644), the phoenix had come to symbolize the empress and, by extension, the *yin*, or female, forces of the universe, just as the dragon had come to represent the emperor and the *yang*, or male, forces. During the Ming and Qing (1644–1911) periods, the two phoenixes in a pair occasionally were both represented with barbed, segmented tails, in which case they were distinguished by their differing numbers of tail filaments, the male with five, the female with but two. Individual, rather than paired, each of the ascending phoenixes that enlivens this silk panel has a segmented tail with five barbed strands; thus, the phoenixes correspond in style to those of China's Song dynasty, corroborating the twelfth to thirteenth century date previously assigned.

The luxury silk fragments represented by this panel appear to be among the earliest to incorporate repeating designs brocaded with gold threads. In that context, they seem to stand midway between the patterned silks of the Tang dynasty—whose repeating designs typically were achieved either through compound twill[23] or damask[24] weaves or through painting[25] or printing[26]—and the brocaded silks that were used for ceremonial dress throughout the Mongol empire during the thirteenth and fourteenth centuries.[27] Because their design units are discrete and because those discrete units rely upon both positive and negative elements for effect, these brocaded silks exhibit an aesthetic kinship to the bowls of russet-glazed Ding ware that were sometimes embellished with cut-gold-leaf designs during the Northern Song period.[28] In addition, the brocaded designs distantly echo the visual effects created by those thin, reticulated sheets of gold and silver that in Han and Tang times were inlaid in *pingtuo* lacquer (better known in the West by the Japanese name of *heidatsu* lacquer), often as decoration on the backs of Tang-dynasty bronze mirrors.[29] Such decorated lacquers typically feature openwork representations of flying birds along with a variety of plants and animals against a black or chocolate brown ground. With their similar representational decorative elements and their preference for gold designs set against assertive monochrome grounds, *pingtuo* lacquers, dark-glazed Ding bowls, and Jin-dynasty brocaded silks share a kindred aesthetic sensibility. In addition, the thirteenth-century, reticulated-gold, phoenix-emblazoned ornament in the collection of Pierre Uldry, Zurich, tellingly reveals that the use of teardrop form phoenix medallions was not limited to textile decoration in the Song, Jin, and Yuan periods.[30]

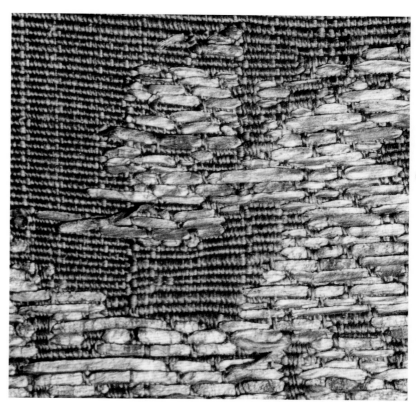

1

[Detail: front]

1

[Detail: back]

27

At least five other closely related brocades are known, all with the same phoenix-and-cloud medallions of teardrop form and all with tightly woven grounds of light blue silk now faded turquoise: one square fragment in the Association pour l'Étude et la Documentation des Textiles d'Asie (AEDTA), Paris;[31] one square fragment in The Cleveland Museum of Art;[32] one very small rectangular fragment in the Uragami Sōkyu-dō Company, Tokyo;[33] and two long narrow fragments in Spink and Son, London.[34] Although the bolts of brocaded silk from which these pieces came conceivably could have been produced on the same loom by the same weavers within a few days of each other, the exact circumstances of their manufacture, not to mention their relationships to each other, remain unknown. Small technical differences in weaves and thread counts, noted below by Martha Winslow Grimm, indicate that these surviving pieces could not have come from one single bolt of silk. The Clague collection panel is comparatively large and in good condition. Because it is the only one that preserves both selvages, the Clague panel is by far the most important of these phoenix-and-cloud decorated silks.

[RDM]

Publications: Claudia Brown, "The Amy S. Clague Collection of Chinese Textiles," *Orientations* 31, no. 2 (February 2000), p. 35, fig. 4.

Technical analysis

Warp: Blue gray silk; slight Z twist; single ply. Count: 66 yarns per centimeter. Step: Irregular. Flaws: in localized areas, warps skip where they should intersect with wefts. *Weft*: Foundation: blue gray silk; no apparent twist; no ply, two to four in a bundle, not twisted together. Count: 24 bundled yarns per centimeter (totaling approximately 52 yarns per centimeter). Step: one pass. Other: wefts float on reverse when not used in weave. Flaws: numerous mistakes in weaving wefts; localized areas exhibit a length of weft yarn piled on surface of textile (because the weft yarn had not been pulled sufficiently tight when woven). Supplementary: gold adhered to animal substrate; no twist; no ply. Other: the top surface of the gold wefts which no longer have gilding are yellow brown in color. Condition: gold is missing from approximately twenty-five per cent of the gold wefts. Gold wefts are broken in many places. Some thread ends push through the textile, emerging (and thus visible) on the obverse. *Weave*: warp-faced tabby. Pass: one paired foundation weft and one brocading weft, except where foundation wefts are floated. Other: brocade is the binding of gold supplementary wefts. On the obverse, the gold wefts are bound by the warps in a 1/8 S twill weave. On the reverse, the gold wefts are unbound and extend from one motif to the next. (However, there is only one example of this in the entire textile.) Condition: Because of photodegradation, the obverse is much lighter in color than the reverse; localized, tan-colored areas of the obverse appear burned; other localized areas show soiling. The textile recently was cleaned and ironed; lack of precision in the ironing resulted in the impression of new creases in the textile surface. The gold supplementary wefts have contracted causing puckering of the foundation weave. *Dyeing*: Yarn dyed. *Selvages*: both selvages are present. Weave: warp-faced tabby. Width: 1 centimeter. Location: along both sides. Other: on both sides the outer edge warp is a bundle of yarns; the other warps in the selvage are thicker than the warps in the body of the textile. The gold supplementary wefts do not extend into the selvages.

Commentary

The Clague panel is very similar to a gold-brocaded silk fragment in the collection of The Cleveland Museum of Art (CMA accession number 1994.292; see New York 1997, pp.118-19, no. 31). The differences are: warp, weft, and supplementary weft counts differ; the Clague panel's foundation wefts are multiple strands in a bundle, whereas the Cleveland fragment's foundation wefts are paired; and the Clague panel has both its selvages. It could not be determined whether or not the Cleveland fragment has the same brown adhesive as the Clague panel.

[MWG]

1   Chemical analysis of fibers from the related silk brocade fragment in the collection of the Association pour l'Étude et la Documentation des Textiles d'Asie, Paris (AEDTA inventory number 3086), see below, allowed Dr. Jan Wouters to conclude that both warp and foundation weft threads were dyed with indigo and madder. Riboud 1995, n.p., appendix, "Dye Analysis" section.

2   Qualitative analysis of gold-faced, supplementary weft threads from the related silk brocade fragment in the collection of the Association pour l'Étude et la Documentation des Textiles d'Asie, Paris (AEDTA inventory number 3086), see below, revealed that they contain gold, iron, copper (or brass), calcium, and potassium. Dominique de Reyer, who did the analysis, notes that all components are indistinctly present in the gold leaf or the organic support. Riboud 1995, n.p., appendix, "Gold Thread Analysis" section.

3   For information on the use of metal threads and animal substrates, see "Metal Threads", chapter 5, pp. 128–138, in Tímár-Balázsy and Eastop 1998; Indictor et al. 1988; Indictor et al. 1989; Kennedy and Maitland 1989; Kohara et al. 1998.

4   For a brief discussion of the circumstances surrounding their survival in Tibet, see Gluckman 1995.

5   To date, known ground colors include white, red, blue, green, yellow, and purple.

6   Watt et al. 1990, pp. 85–86; Riboud 1995.

7   Heilongjiang Provincial Institute 1989; Zhu 1990.

8   The tomb of Prince Qi lies just outside Chengzi, a village near Juyuan, which is located a few miles straight north of the city of Acheng. In southeastern Heilongjiang province, Acheng is roughly 675 miles northeast of Beijing and is about twenty miles southeast of Harbin, the provincial capital.

9   New York 1997, pp. 107–125; Ogasawara 1989; Krahl 1997.

10   New York 1997, p. 108.

11   New York 1997, pp. 108–109.

12   Watt et al. 1990, pp. 85–86.

13   For background information on Chinese taste for gold, see Bunker 1993.

14   See Ebrey 1999, p. 78, fig. 8.

15   See Krahl 1997, pp. 50–51, figs. 12, 14.

16   Chai and Chai 1967, vol. 1, p. 384.

17   Although phoenix-like birds frequently appear on ritual bronzes of the Shang (c. 16th century B.C.—c. 1028 B.C.) and Zhou (c. 1027–221 B.C.) dynasties, the exact identity of those birds remains uncertain, so it is difficult to pinpoint the date of the first appearance of the phoenix in Chinese visual arts.

18   See Cambridge 1996, p. 83, no. 2. The Koreans adopted this image of the striding phoenix late in their Three Kingdoms period (traditionally, 57 B.C.–A.D. 668), imbuing it with a grace and vitality seldom encountered in China. See Kim and Lee 1974, p. 224, no. 196.

19   See San Francisco 1983, p. 44, color plate 20, no. 63.

20   See Simcox 1994, p. 38, fig. 5; Spink and Son 1999, n.p., nos. 1–2.

21   See Cambridge 1996, p. 241, no. 96, and p. 243, no. 97.

22   See New York 1997, p. 197, figs. 82–93, and p. 197, no. 60; Rawson 1984, p. 101, fig. 82; Simcox 1989, p. 24, fig. 8; Simcox 1994, p. 39, fig. 6; Cambridge 1996, p. 254, no. 103.

23   See New York 1997, pp. 30–35, nos. 1–5.

24   See New York 1997, p. 36, no. 5.

25   See New York 1997, pp. 40–41, no. 7.

26   See Machida 1988, pp. 66–72, nos. 1–20.

27   Watt et al. 1990, p. 85.

28   See Cambridge 1996, p. 109, no. 15; Tokyo National Museum 1994, p. 111, pls. 156–57; Hasebe 1977, pp. 26–27, nos. 19–21.

29   See Mowry 1981, p. 56, no. 1979.119; Freer Gallery of Art 1972, n.p., pl. 26, and p. 155, no. 26; Dayton 1984, p. 91, no. 59.

30   See Zurich 1994, p. 240, no. 288.

31   AEDTA inventory number 3086. See Riboud 1995, p. 93, fig. 2 and p. 95, figs. 8–9; Krahl 1997, p. 45, fig. 1.

32   CMA accession number 1994.292. See New York 1997, pp. 118–119, no. 31.

33   See Ogasawara 1989, p. 42, figs. 12, 12a, 12b.

34   See Spink and Son 1994, n.p., no. 10; Spink and Son 1999, n.p., no. 5.

1

2 Rectangular Silk Fragment with Dragon-and-Flaming-Pearl Medallions against a Ground of Scrolling Clouds

Yuan dynasty (1279–1368)
> Silk brocade; royal blue silk ground of dyed yarns in tabby weave, the ground interwoven
> in brocade weave with flat strips of double-layered paper faced with gold leaf
H. 22.0 cm; W. 27.5 cm

30 Lushly decorated, this small rectangular silk fragment preserves one whole cusped circular medallion representing a coiled dragon pursuing a flaming pearl amidst cloud wisps, and, in the same horizontal row, half of another, identical, repeat medallion; portions of two additional medallions appear in the staggered but now-truncated row at the bottom. All of the decoration is brocaded in gold against a tightly woven ground of royal blue silk. In the single whole medallion, a three-clawed dragon strides toward the proper right, his alert gaze fixed on the flaming jewel, his front legs placed so that the border reads as a ground line; the dragon's body coils counter-clockwise, his hind legs appearing at the top, the tip of his barbed tail approaching the flames emanating from the jewel. A sinewy line of reserved blue silk ground together with a series of brocaded triangles clearly and effectively defines the dragon's knobbed spine. A narrow inner border joins a wide, solid, outer border to frame each sixteen-lobed medallion; broad cloud scrolls fill the spaces between medallions, leaving few areas undecorated. A single three-taloned claw in the fragmentary medallion in the textile's lower proper right corner indicates that the truncated medallions also depicted dragons, even if too little evidence survives to determine the dragons' orientations; if they featured similar dragon-and-pearl motifs, the truncated medallions may have been top-bottom mirror images of the single surviving whole medallion rather than left-right reversals. This luxurious textile relies upon gold-faced supplementary wefts to create the brocaded designs; those supplementary wefts are wide, flat strips of double-layer paper (rather than animal substrate) to which bright gold leaf has been applied over a ground of bole[1] on the obverse. The rose pink bole is visible in areas where the gold is abraded; the ochre-hued paper is visible on the reverse and in tiny areas of the obverse where both gold and bole are abraded. Both foundation and supplementary wefts are continuous across this textile; no wefts—neither foundation nor supplementary—float on the reverse, even in the brocaded areas. Three foundation wefts bundled together serve as a single weft in the weave; although it produces a ribbed effect in the foundation weave, bundling of the wefts was necessary to compensate for the width of the interwoven gold-faced supplementary wefts. The supplementary wefts appear only on the obverse in the brocaded areas and only on the reverse in the undecorated areas. Every third warp passes over the supplementary wefts, binding them to the foundation weave. In this arrangement, no wefts need to float. Because of this weave structure, the design on the back is a reverse of that on the front; thus the decoration is a left-right mirror image of that on the front and the colors are reversed, the background appearing brocaded, the pattern reserved in royal blue.

2

[Front]

32

2

[Detail: back]

Introduced during the Liao and Jin dynasties, silks with gold-brocaded medallions continued to be prized during the Mongol Yuan dynasty, when they not only were used for official and ceremonial dress but were popularized throughout the Mongol empire.[2] Paintings of the Yuan dynasty depicting Mongols hunting often show officials wearing garments of brightly colored silk enlivened with gold decoration.[3] Wherever this fragment of brocade might have been used, its reliance on a paper, rather than an animal, substrate for the gold-faced supplementary wefts suggests that the bolt of silk from which it came must have been woven in China proper, even if its exact place of manufacture cannot be pinpointed.

Like the phoenixes that embellish the Jin-dynasty silk brocade (number 1), dragons, or *long*, are Chinese in origin, though their appreciation was not limited to China itself. Regarded already in late Zhou and Han cosmology as one of the four directional animals, the green dragon represents the east, alongside the red phoenix of the south, the white tiger of the west, and the intertwined black snake and tortoise of the north. Dragons are usually considered symbols of the *yang*, or male, forces of the universe, the *yin*, or female, forces represented by the phoenix. During the Ming and Qing dynasties, the five-clawed dragon served as the emperor's insignia, so that many works destined for the palace bear that emblem.

The pairing of dragon and jewel seems to represent a combination of elements from two separate traditions, the dragon from Chinese mythology and the jewel from Buddhist iconography. The jewel, often termed a pearl in English, derives from the Buddhist *ruyi baozhu*, or wish-granting jewel (Sanskrit, *cintâmani*) that is held by a number of Buddhist deities, including the Bodhisattvas Ruyilun Guanyin (Cintâmani-cakra Avalokitesvara) and Dizang (Ksitigarbha). The *ruyi baozhu* is not a pearl in the strict sense of the term, but a talismanic jewel that symbolizes transcendent wisdom and can grant every wish. The flames surrounding the jewel symbolize its magical powers. Expanding upon Buddhist tradition, Chinese lore maintains that the magical jewel is obtained not only from the relics of a Buddha, but from the dragon-king of the sea or from the head of the mythical hybrid creature known as a *makara*.[4] The motif of dragon-and-jewel thus associates the dragon with knowledge and supernatural powers; as an emblem on official robes, it associates those attributes with office holders.

Dragons of various types ornament Neolithic painted pottery and Bronze Age ritual vessels. The distant ancestor of the slender, scaled, serpentine creature with long neck and tail that we recognize as the Chinese dragon first appeared during the Warring States or Han period.[5] Linked with water, particularly with life-giving rain for the farmers' crops, the dragon is typically presented amidst clouds and is often shown striding above cresting waves. The dragon as magical or auspicious serpent (*ling she*) had been paired with the jewel in Chinese literature since the Han dynasty.[6] The earliest coiled dragons appeared in the Tang, just as the first visual pairing of dragon and pearl may have occurred in the Tang, as suggested by the ornament on some Tang silver vessels and by the placement of the dragon in relation to the hemispherical knob on the backs of some Tang-dynasty bronze mirrors.[7] The motif's popularity expanded in the Song and Jin periods and then soared in the Yuan. Favored as a subject for painting on paper and

34

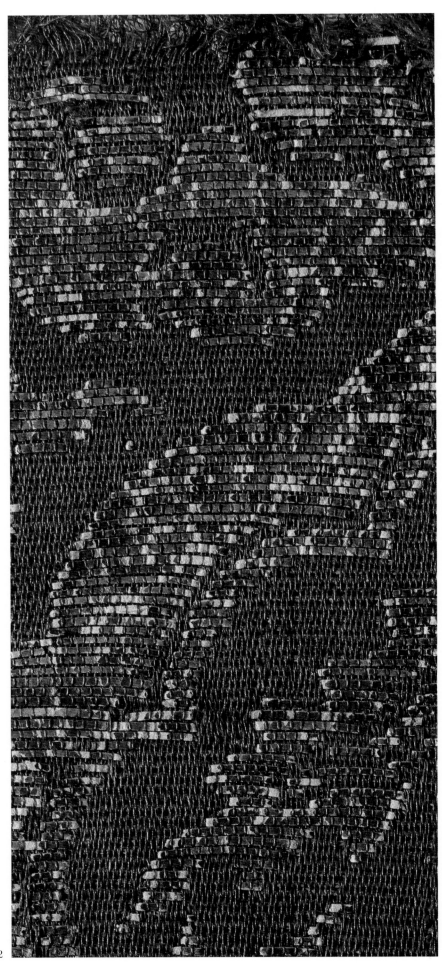

2
[Detail]

silk during the Tang and Song dynasties, the dragon has been among the most prominent motifs in textiles and in the decorative arts since the Five Dynasties period. The dragon-and-pearl motifs that enliven Liao silver vessels[8] and Jin porcelains[9] are close relatives of those woven into Jin and Yuan silks.

Silks with gold-brocaded, dragon-and-pearl roundels had appeared in the Jin dynasty, as evinced by an example in the collection of The Metropolitan Museum of Art, New York.[10] Like the Clague collection's contemporaneous gold-brocaded phoenix panel (number 1), the Metropolitan's Jin-dynasty, coiled-dragon textile has individualized medallions set against an unembellished ground; its circular medallions, which lack borders, are arranged in staggered rows, the dragons' left-right orientation alternating from row to row. By contrast, the present Yuan-dynasty brocaded silk fragment from the Clague collection appears entirely decorated. Although the Clague fragment's coiled dragons themselves differ little from those in The Metropolitan Museum's Jin-dynasty example, the heavy borders enclosing the medallions and the numerous scrolling clouds that fill the background areas impart a very pronounced visual effect to the Clague fragment.

35

Although the sumptuous brocades of the Jin and Yuan dynasties appear similar on first inspection, due to their very tight weaves and their gold designs set against brightly colored grounds, their styles clearly distinguish them. The most obvious difference in the brocades of these two periods is the density of the decoration. In Jin-dynasty silks, the decoration is organized into staggered rows of repeating design elements with ample space between the rhythmically spaced elements, so that there is a happy balance between decorated and undecorated areas (number 1). As this fragment reveals, even though the lobed medallions are arranged in staggered rows, the decoration tends to cover virtually the entire surface of Yuan-dynasty brocaded silks, so that they appear lush and complex. Although they seldom have borders, the repeating design elements of Jin silks characteristically assume simple, self-contained, geometric configurations—circles, triangles, and teardrop-shapes, for example. By contrast, the principal motifs of Yuan brocades typically appear within circular medallions, often with cusped edges and wide borders, the medallions set against a heavily textured ground. With their simpler design schemes, Jin-dynasty, gold-brocaded silks seem austere and restrained. In terms of technique, the decorated areas of Jin brocades show floating foundation wefts and discontinuous supplementary wefts on the reverse, but in Yuan-period pieces, both foundation and supplementary wefts are continuous, with no floating wefts; in Yuan pieces, however, the foundation wefts tend to be bundled in order to accommodate the wide, gold-faced supplementary wefts, with the result that the finished fabric appears lightly ribbed. In addition, the substrates for the gold supplementary wefts differ: Jin examples typically have sheep- or goat-hide leather substrates but Yuan pieces characteristically have paper substrates.

Though reversed, the dragon-and-pearl medallion in this brocaded fragment is otherwise identical to the dragon-and-pearl medallion in a Yuan-dynasty, lampas-weave silk textile in the collection of The Cleveland Museum of Art.[11] In addition, this fragment's lobed roundels and heavily textured ground are akin to those that adorn the long, patterned fabric, perhaps of brocaded silk, that covers the wooden bench upon which the Buddhist layman Weimo (Sanskrit, Vimalakirti) sits in the 1308–dated handscroll by Wang Zhenpeng (active c. 1280–1329) representing *Vimalakirti and the Doctrine of Nonduality* and now in the collection of The Metropolitan Museum of Art, New York.[12] The Clague silk fragment's cusped medallions find parallels not only in Yuan lobed silver vessels,[13] a staple of Yuan silversmiths, but in the ogival panels that were a popular feature in Yuan-period architectural decoration (the ogival panels sometimes boasting dragon-and-pearl motifs).[14] Even the cloud heads surrounding the dragon medallions relate to the geometric decoration carved in Yuan-period, black-and-red lacquer pieces.[15] Thus, Yuan silks with gold-brocaded decoration relate not just to other Yuan textiles but to all the arts produced in that era of great artistic foment. In concluding, however, it also should be noted that designs of lobed medallions set against densely patterned grounds had already appeared by the Northern Song period—as evinced by the Northern Song sutra container recovered in 1966 at the Huiguang Pagoda site in Rui'an, Zhejiang province[16]—even if such designs did not find their way into textile decoration until the Yuan dynasty.

[RDM]

Technical analysis

Warp: royal blue silk; slight Z twist; single ply. Count: 160 yarns per centimeter. Step: irregular. Other: warps are paired and sometimes tripled. Condition: one area in the center of the textile exhibits broken warps; raveled warps that are frayed extend from the four edges. *Weft*: Foundation: royal blue silk; Z twist; no ply (bundled yarns not twisted together). Count: 18 yarns per centimeter. Step: one pass. Other: three wefts bundled together serve as one weft when woven. Condition: a whitish substance adheres to the royal blue foundation wefts. Supplementary: gold adhered to one side of a flat, double layered paper; no twist; no ply. Color: bright gold. Count: 6 strips per centimeter. Step: one pass. Other: adhesive is reddish brown in color. Condition: numerous breaks of the gold on both the obverse and the reverse. *Weave*: Warp-faced tabby. Pass: one foundation weft and one brocading weft paired together. Other: brocade is the binding of the gold supplementary wefts. Every third warp passes over the gold supplementary weft, holding it to the foundation weave. The gold supplementary wefts do not float on the reverse side of the textile; when not needed for the brocade pattern, they move to the reverse but are still held by warp yarns. Bundled wefts produce a ribbed effect in the foundation weave; these thick wefts compensate for the width of the gold supplementary wefts. Condition: There is a line of compressed spots and perforations along one edge where previously there were sewing-machine stitches. *Dyeing*: Yarn dyed. *Selvages*: none remaining.

[MWG]

1 Traditionally prepared with animal glue, bole is a variety of hematite-loaded clay that is used as an under layer, or ground, in gilding. Exceptionally smooth, it serves as a cushion under gold leaf that is to be burnished. Due to the abundant hematite, bole is typically red or shell pink, though it can be blue, yellow, or even, rarely, other colors. I am grateful to Marjorie B. Cohn and Craigen Bowen, my colleagues at the Harvard University Art Museums, for this concise definition of bole.

2 Watt et al. 1990, pp. 85–86.

3 Watt et al. 1990, p. 86. For an example of such a painting, see New York 1996, p. 270, pl. 138, and p. 262, pl. 138 (detail).

4 Soothill 1937, p. 211.

5 See San Francisco 1987, p. 174, pl. 68, and p. 180, pl. 70d.

6 New York 1997, p. 116.

7 See Rawson 1984, p. 97, fig. 76 (right). James C. Y. Watt has suggested that "The dragon-and-pearl motif, particularly that with a coiled dragon, may have had its origin in Central Asia, with remote precedents in the late Roman world." New York 1997, p. 116, text and also footnote 1.

8 See Inner Mongolia 1987, p. 12, fig. 16, and n.p., pl. 6, no. 2.

9 See Mowry 1981, p. 65, accession number 1979.140; San Francisco 1983, p. 99, no. 78.

10 See New York 1997, pp. 116–17, no. 30 (MMA accession number 1989.205). Also compare Riboud 1995, p. 94, figs. 3–5; Krahl 1997, p. 48, fig. 7.

11 CMA accession number 1995.73. See New York 1997, p. 153, no. 42.

12 See Fong 1992, pp. 332–333, pl. 73.

13 See Sickman 1957, p. 82, fig. 7a.

14 See Murata and Fujieda 1955, vol. 2, n.p., pl. 20; New York 1997, p. 196, fig. 82; Rawson 1984, p. 101, fig. 82.

15 See New York 1996, p. 457, pls. 259–260.

16 The sutra container is now in the collection of the Zhejiang Provincial Museum, Hangzhou. See New York 1998, n.p., no. 73.

3 Rectangular Silk Panel with a Buddhist Mantra

Ming dynasty, mid-15th–early 17th century
Silk brocade; rust red silk ground of dyed yarns in tabby weave, the ground interwoven
in brocade weave with flat strips of double-layered paper faced with gold leaf
H. 21.5 cm; W. 66.5 cm, including selvages

This sumptuous, horizontally oriented, rectangular silk panel features a Buddhist mantra in Lantsa-script characters, the single row of seven characters enclosed within a narrow border on all four sides. Both text and framing band are brocaded in gold against a tightly woven ground of rust red silk. This textile relies upon gold-faced supplementary wefts to create the brocaded design; those supplementary wefts are wide, flat strips of double-layer paper to which gold leaf has been applied over a ground of bole.[1] The ivory-hued paper is visible on the reverse and in tiny areas of the obverse where the gold is abraded. The selvages along the left and right edges indicate that this panel preserves the full breadth of the original fabric. In addition, they reveal the width of the loom on which the fabric was woven, just as they unequivocally distinguish the warp and weft yarns. The rust red color is a little more intense on the back of this panel, indicating that the reverse has been better protected from light than the obverse, which shows slight fading.[2] Both foundation and supplementary wefts are continuous across this textile; no wefts—neither foundation nor supplementary—float on the reverse, even in the brocaded areas. Seven foundation wefts bundled together serve as a single weft in the weave. Although it produces a ribbed effect in the finished fabric, bundling of the wefts was necessary to compensate for the width of the interwoven gold-faced supplementary wefts. The supplementary wefts appear only in the brocaded areas on the obverse and only in the background areas on the reverse. Every fourth warp passes over the supplementary wefts, binding them to the foundation weave. In this arrangement, no wefts need to float. Because of this weave structure, the design on the back is a reverse of that on the front; thus the text is a left-right mirror image of that on the front and the colors are reversed, the background appearing brocaded, the text reserved in rust red.

This textile's seven brocaded characters represent the transliteration of a Sanskrit invocation or prayer; they are written in Lantsa script, an Indic script used in Nepal and Tibet for Buddhist invocations and prayers—and also in China for Tibetan-style Buddhist invocations and prayers. The first six syllables comprise a mantra that, from left to right, reads "Om mani padme hum" and that is conventionally translated "O, the jewel in the lotus." The seventh syllable, which reads "hri", is a "seed character" or "seed syllable" (Sanskrit, *bija-mantra*) that symbolizes the Bodhisattva Avalokitesvara (Chinese, Guanyin Pusa), with whom this mantra traditionally is associated.[3] To preserve their efficacy, all mantras and *dharanis* (invocations) are spoken or chanted using the original Sanskrit sounds, even when translated into Chinese or Tibetan, as the sounds themselves are believed to hold mystical powers, even if their Sanskrit meanings lie beyond the comprehension of those who hear them.[4]

Although its shape and proportions suggest that it once might have served as a cover for a Buddhist sutra, or holy text, this panel most likely was originally made as part of a vertical banner that hung in a Tibetan Buddhist temple or in a Lamaist temple in China. In fact, its striking similarity to each of the eight identical tiers of a banner available on the London market in the mid–1990s strongly implies that this panel was cut from just such a banner.[5] Despite their similarities, slight differences indicate that the Clague panel was not cut from the London banner: the characters in the London banner are even closer together than those in the Clague panel and they are a little taller and a little more elongated, with the result that there is even less space between the tops of the characters and the upper border. In addition, the longest of the characters' curving tails touch the lower border in the London banner, just as the two superscript elements touch its upper border; in the Clague panel, by contrast, characters and borders do not touch. If it came from such a banner, the Clague panel likely would have been one of eight identical, integrally woven, horizontal registers, since the number eight is considered auspicious in Buddhist numerology. When finished on the loom, the original fabric might have been much longer than a stretch of eight registers, permitting numerous eight-tier banners to be cut from it.

38

3

The lack of comparative material makes the dating of such silk brocades very difficult. Although the London banner formerly was attributed to the thirteenth century,[6] its bold style— bordered registers with large characters that expand to fill all available space—argue for a date in the Ming dynasty. In fact, the results of a radiocarbon test conducted by Timothy Jull at The University of Arizona NSF-Arizona AMS Facility, Tucson, on a small sample removed from it indicate that this panel dates between the mid-fifteenth and early seventeenth centuries.[7] In the context of Chinese Buddhist paraphernalia, it should be noted that this panel's red and gold palette finds parallels in Song-dynasty sutra containers[8] and early Ming sutra covers,[9] the most sumptuous of which boast designs embellished in gold on a ground of red-lacquered wood.

Although they surely were not made as scroll-mounting silks, brocades of this exact design have been incorporated into the mountings of some Buddhist scrolls preserved in Tibet, the panels perhaps salvaged from damaged banners or perhaps cut from intact banners and then piously set within the scrolls to honor important deities. Now preserved in the Tibet Museum, Lhasa, a Xixia- (1032–1227) or Southern Song-period *kesi*-tapestry image representing the deity Budong Mingwang (Sanskrit, Acala Candamaharosana)—The Immovable One, One of the Five Great Kings of Wisdom—has gold-brocaded silk panels of identical color, design, and weave immediately above and below the image.[10] Although the present mounting unquestionably is much later than the *kesi* image itself, the date that those brocaded panels were incorporated into the scroll's mounting is not only unknown but probably unknowable. Though it sheds no light on the date of the Clague panel, the Budong scroll illustrates both the reverence in which these precious textiles traditionally were held and diverse uses that they historically served.

[RDM]

Publications: Claudia Brown, "The Amy S. Clague Collection of Chinese Textiles," *Orientations* 31, no. 2 (February 2000), p. 35, fig. 5.

Technical analysis

Warp: Rust red silk; slight Z twist; single ply. Count: 156 yarns per centimeter. Step: irregular. Condition: Five areas of broken warps and wefts. Many warps binding the gold supplementary wefts to the foundation weave are broken on the obverse but remain intact on the reverse. *Weft*: Foundation: Rust red silk; slight Z twist; no ply (bundled yarns not twisted together). Count: 140 wefts per centimeter. Step: one pass. Other: Wefts are bundled. Seven wefts bundled together serve as one weft when woven. Supplementary: gold adhered to flat, double-layered paper; no twist; no ply. Color: light gold. Count: 20 yarns per centimeter. Step: one pass. Condition: gold is missing from approximately five per cent of the supplementary wefts. Numerous breaks in the gold leaf on both obverse and reverse. *Weave*: Tabby, brocaded. Pass: one foundation weft bundle and one brocading weft. The thickness of the weft bundles produces a ribbed effect in the finished fabric. Other: brocade is the binding of the gold supplementary wefts. Every fourth warp passes over the gold supplementary weft, holding it to the foundation weave. The gold supplementary wefts do not float on the reverse side of the textile; when not needed for the brocade pattern, they move to the reverse but are still held by warp yarns. The gold supplementary wefts do not turn into the next shed; rather, they were cut so that they stop at the inner edge of each selvage. Bundled wefts produce a ribbed effect in the foundation weave; these thick wefts compensate for the width of the gold supplementary wefts. Condition: Five areas of broken and missing warps and wefts. New fabric of matching color and fiber has been placed as fill in those areas with broken and missing yarns. Very soiled; localized surface spots of wax on the obverse. *Dyeing*: Yarn dyed. *Selvages*: Both selvages are present. Weave: tabby. Width: 0.6 centimeter. Location: along both sides. Other: The selvages are composed of 17 bundles of warps; the two warp bundles on the outermost edge are thicker than the others. The warp yarns in the selvages are the same in color as the foundation warp yarns in the main portion of the textile. The foundation wefts turn around the outermost warp. The gold supplementary wefts do not turn into the next shed; rather, they were cut so that they stop at the inner edge of each selvage. Condition: Good except for two diagonal cuts in the proper left warp.

[MWG]

1 For a definition of bole, see number 2, note 1.

2 In addition, careful examination of individual threads—particularly those along the (recently cut) top and bottom edges, those lying under the gold-faced supplementary wefts, and those concealed within the weave—reveals that the textile originally was a little brighter in color than the now slightly faded obverse.

3 I am grateful to Professor Richard Salomon, Department of Asian Languages and Literature, University of Washington, Seattle, who identified this mantra and its Lantsa script. E-mail message dated 4 January 2000 from Professor Salomon to Professor Claudia Brown, Department of Art History, Arizona State University, Tempe. For information on the mantra "Om mani padme hum" and the historically changing explanations of its meaning, see "The Spell", chap. 4, pp. 114–134 in Lopez 1998.

4 Pal and Meech-Pekarik 1988, p. 258.

5 See Spink and Son 1994, p. 19, no. 14.

6 See Spink and Son 1994, p. 19, no. 14.

7 Sample date number: AA-31549. According to Timothy Jull, on the basis of the radiocarbon tests, this textile can be assigned to the period 1447–1612 with sixty eight per cent confidence or to the period 1439–1629 with ninety five per cent confidence.
Letter dated 23 February 1999 from A. J. T. Jull, The University of Arizona NSF-Arizona AMS Facility, Tucson, to Claudia Brown, Research Curator for Asian Art, Phoenix Art Museum.
For information on the use of radiocarbon analysis in dating textiles, see Jull and Donahue 1990.

8 See New York 1998, n.p., no. 73.

9 See New York 1991, pp. 116–118, no. 49; Lee 1995, p. 76, fig. 11.

10 See New York 1998, n.p., no. 85; Huang 1985, pp. 206–207, no. 193; Henss 2000, p. 65, right column . Although all three of these sources illustrate the *kesi* image of Budong, the related panels of brocaded silk are clearly visible only in New York 1998 , n.p., no. 85.

4 Rectangular Silk Altar, Table, or Desk Frontal with Pleated Valance and with Decoration of Confronting *Makaras*

Ming dynasty, late 15th–early 16th century, perhaps Chenghua period (1465–1487)
Silk brocade; dark marine blue silk ground of dyed yarns in four-end satin weave,
the ground interwoven in brocade weave with polychrome silk yarns and with
bundled silk threads wrapped with flat paper strips faced with gold leaf
H. 84.5 cm; W. 109.0 cm (Selvage-to-selvage width of each lower panel: 54.5 cm)

Perhaps for a Buddhist altar or perhaps for a formal table or a magistrate's desk, this rectangular frontal of brocaded silk comprises a rectangular main panel crowned by a narrow, pleated valance, the valance stitched horizontally to the top of the main panel. The main panel itself further comprises two square halves joined down the panel's center by a vertical seam. Brocaded in polychrome silk yarns, two confronting, four-clawed *makaras*—mythical horned creatures, seemingly half dragon, half feline, which have only front legs, their hind quarters dissolving into floral scrolls—emblazon this frontal's main panel, a single stylized lotus blossom issuing from their open mouths. Tongues of flame emanate from the *makaras*, signaling their extraordinary powers, while mushroom-head clouds hover over the open blossom. Stacked vertically, the *bajixiang*, or Eight Auspicious Emblems, frame the frontal's outer edges, while jeweled chains alternate with fluttering red tassels to border its lower edge. The two halves of the main panel are bilaterally symmetrical, except for slight differences in the placement of the cloud heads at the center and in the arrangement of the colors (most notably in the border of stacked auspicious emblems). The brocaded valance—a single, continuous stretch of pleated silk meticulously folded to form seven panels—echoes the design of the main panel: two *makaras* confront in the double-width central panel, flanked on either side by three *makaras* striding toward the proper right, each *makara* with a half lotus blossom issuing from its mouth. Borders of *leiwen*, or squared spirals, serve as ground lines on which the *makaras* stride, the lappets descending from the *leiwen* bands underscoring the distinction between valance and main panel. Both selvages are present on each of the two halves of the main panel, though the selvages at the panel's center are visible only from the reverse, since they were folded under in stitching the seam; the top and bottom edges of the main panel were cut. Visible only on the reverse, as it was folded under in stitching the seam, a selvage appears along the lower edge of the valance; the top and outside edges of the valance were cut. In both the main panel and the valance, the brocaded designs are interwoven into the dark marine blue ground of silk satin, using supplementary wefts of both polychrome silk yarns and gold-faced threads. Used for the lotus blossoms at the centers of the main panel and of the valance and also for the descending lappets at the lower edge of the valance, the gold-faced threads in this frontal are more complex than those in the silk textiles of catalog numbers 1, 2, and 3; that is, these "gold threads" are bundles of white or yellow silk fibers which have been tightly wrapped with flat strips of paper substrate to which dull-hued gold leaf has been applied over a ground of pink bole.[1] Numerous weft threads float across the reverse of this textile to accommodate the brocaded designs. Comparison of this textile's front and back faces reveals that the brightly colored silk yarns used for the brocaded designs have faded slightly on the front.

42

4

4

[Detail]

Buddhist altars were ceremonially draped with vestments from earliest times. Paintings and woodblock prints indicate that although altar frontals typically lacked valances during the Tang and Five Dynasties periods,[2] such valances had become integral components by the Song.[3] Paintings and woodblock prints further reveal that frontals remarkably similar to those used for Buddhist altars also were used for formal tables and magistrates' desks during the Ming and Qing periods.[4] In Ming and Qing pictorial representations, the valances are characteristically pleated, sometimes with small, narrow pleats, sometimes with wide pleats akin to those in the Clague frontal. In such paintings and prints, the frontals cover not only the fronts but the sides of the altars, desks, and tables. Those depictions thus raise the question of whether the Clague frontal originally might have included additional panels; interesting as it is, that question cannot be answered here. Frontals depicted in paintings and prints conventionally sport stylized floral patterns, rather than the *makaras* that enliven the Clague frontal.

Popular in the Ming and Qing periods, the *makaras* that ornament this frontal—and the *bajixiang* emblems that border its main panel—were introduced into China from Tibet during the Yuan dynasty. The *makara*, a hybrid sea creature, originated more than two thousand years ago in India, where it was regarded as a symbol of fertility, as suggested by the floral scrolls that issue from its mouth. Incorporated into early Indian Buddhist art, along with *yaksas, yaksis,* and other fertility emblems, *makara* imagery found its way to all the lands where Buddhism spread.[5] Like Tibetan Buddhism itself, the motif was introduced to China, together with a host of new deities, motifs, and ritual paraphernalia, during the Yuan dynasty, as evinced by its appearance on the cut-stone, arched, pagoda base that was constructed in 1345 and that survives near Juyongguan, a Great Wall gate to the northwest of Beijing.[6] The *makara* was viewed as a type of dragon in China—where it was variously termed a *yinglong* or *kuilong* (that is, a *ying* dragon or *kui* dragon)—so that it came to appear in religious and secular contexts alike. It enjoyed its greatest popularity during the Ming dynasty, when it was often employed as decoration on porcelain vessels, particularly on those made at Jingdezhen, Jiangxi province.

The *makaras* on this frontal are remarkably similar to those on blue-and-white[7] and *doucai*-enameled porcelains[8] made during the Chenghua reign (1465–1487) of the Ming dynasty; in fact, because the *makaras* on this frontal are almost identical to those on a Chenghua-period, *doucai*-enameled, small jar that was reconstructed from shards recently excavated at Zhushan, Jingdezhen, this frontal can now safely be assigned to the late fifteenth or early sixteenth century.[9] Their elephant-trunk snouts, bulging eyes, pointed tongues, needle-sharp teeth, stylized bodies, and floral-scroll tails make the *makaras* in those two works virtually interchangeable. Even the *bajixiang* images along the left and right borders correspond very closely to those that embellish Chenghua-period, *doucai*-enameled porcelains, thus bolstering the attribution of this frontal to the late fifteenth or early sixteenth century.[10] The results of a radiocarbon test conducted by Timothy Jull at the The University of Arizona NSF-Arizona AMS Facility, Tucson, on a small sample removed from it confirm that this frontal dates between the mid-fifteenth and mid-seventeenth centuries.[11] From a technical perspective, this handsome frontal attests that from the fifteenth century onward bundles of silk fibers wrapped with gold-faced paper increasingly supplanted the flat strips of gold-faced paper that were interwoven into the "metallic-thread" brocades of earlier periods (compare numbers 1–3).

[RDM]

Publications: Paul Champkins, Jacqueline Simcox, et al., *The Minor Arts of China* IV, dealer's cat., Spink and Son, London, 1989, p. 101, no. 38.

Technical analysis

Warp: Dark marine blue silk; S twist; 2 ply, Z. Count: 54 yarns per centimeter. Condition: Many damaged warp yarns throughout the textile. *Weft*: The weft yarns include one foundation weft and two different supplementary wefts. Foundation: dark marine blue silk — however, note that the valance differs slightly in having brown silk yarns mixed with the dark marine blue to create the foundation wefts; slight Z twist; 2 ply, S. Count: 24 yarns per centimeter. Other: The foundation wefts of the valance and of the two, seam-linked, lower panels are the same, except for the inclusion of brown yarns in the valance's foundation weft. Supplementary: There are two types of supplementary weft yarns; the two types differ greatly from each other. Type-one supplementary: polychrome silk; no apparent twist; no ply (bundled yarns not twisted together). Count: 13 yarns per centimeter. Other: The weaving pattern is one warp over weft, four warps under weft. Type-two supplementary: Bundled silk fibers—some yellow, some white—wrapped within paper strips faced with dull-hued gold leaf; Z twist; no ply (bundled yarns not twisted together). Count: 14 to 17 yarns per centimeter, the count varying depending upon the motif. Other: The weaving pattern is one warp over weft, four warps under weft. Condition: worn on the surface. Although the gold is missing in localized areas, the substrate remains structurally strong, thus preserving the bundled yarns in good condition. *Weave*: Ground fabric is four-end satin with supplementary wefts in a brocade weave. Other: The warps are vertically oriented in two seam-linked lower panels but the warps are horizontally oriented in the valance. Flaws: There are numerous weaving flaws throughout the fabric. *Dyeing*: Yarn dyed. *Selvages*: Both selvages are present on each of the seam-linked, lower panels; only one selvage is present on the valance. Weave: 2/1 twill. Width: 0.8 centimeter. Location: Each of the two lower panels has two selvages, one along either side; two of those selvages are folded under where they meet at the center seam and thus are hidden from view. The valance has one selvage along its bottom edge; it is concealed within the horizontal seam that links the valance to the two lower panels. Other: The selvage warp yarns are much thicker than the warp yarns in the main part of the ground fabric. Every other weft yarn wraps around the outermost warp yarn. Condition: Yarn pulls resulting in a slightly misshapen fabric.

Commentary

This textile is in three pieces. A seam links the lower two panels together in the center of the textile. The valance is one piece seamed horizontally at the top edge to the two lower panels. The valance has six vertical pleats.

[MWG]

1   It should be noted that the golden outlines describing the jeweled chains and fluttering red tassels in the main panel's lower border are golden yellow silk threads, not the bundles of silk fibers wrapped in flat strips of paper surfaced with gold leaf discussed above. For information on the use of metal threads of this type, see "Metal Threads", chapter 5, pp. 128–138, in Tímár-Balázsy and Eastop 1998.

2   See Machida 1988, p. 26, top fig.; Fong 1992, p. 342, fig. 142.

3   See Fong 1992, pp. 338–339, figs. pls. 74 c–f; Machida 1988, p. 26, bottom figure, p. 80, fig. 1, p. 82, fig. 5.

4   See Machida 1988, p. 115, fig. 26.

5   It should be noted that some *kesi*-tapestry panels woven in Eastern Central Asian in the eleventh or twelfth century incorporate dragons whose truncated bodies and elephant-trunk snouts indicate that they were influenced by *makara* imagery. See New York 1997, pp. 66–69, no. 14 and fig. 22.

6   See Murata and Fujieda 1955, vol. 2, n.p., pls. 4, 6.

7   See Taipei 1977, n.p., nos. 49, 72, 101; Hong Kong 1993, pp. 210–11, no. C61.

8   See Taipei 1977, n.p., no. 44; Hong Kong 1993, pp. 260–261, no. C86, pp. 304–305, no. C108.

9   See Hong Kong 1993, pp. 304–305, no. C108.

10 See Hong Kong 1993, pp. 308–309, no. C110, pp. 334–335, no. C123. Also see an unpublished, Chenghua-period, intact, *doucai*-enameled small jar in the collection of the Harvard University Art Museums (1979.444) that is similar to the reconstructed jar illustrated in Hong Kong 1993, p. 309, no. C110.

11 Sample date number: AA-31551. According to Timothy Jull, on the basis of the radiocarbon tests, this textile can be assigned to the period 1441–1606 with sixty eight per cent confidence or to the period 1429–1629 with ninety five per cent confidence. Letter dated 23 February 1999 from A. J. T. Jull, The University of Arizona NSF–Arizona AMS Facility, Tucson, to Claudia Brown, Research Curator for Asian Art, Phoenix Art Museum.

5 Long, Rectangular Panel of Silk with Decoration of Eight Auspicious Emblems (*Bajixiang*) amidst Scrolling Clouds

Ming dynasty, probably second half 16th century
  Silk brocade; dark navy blue silk ground of dyed yarns in four-end satin weave,
  the ground interwoven in brocade weave with polychrome silk yarns and with
  flat gold leaf adhered to dark tan substrate yarns
H. 266.5 cm; W. 30.5 cm

This long, vertically oriented, rectangular panel of silk boasts thirteen rows of cloud heads brocaded in bright colors against a tightly woven ground of midnight blue silk. The staggered rows alternate in number of cloud heads, including either two whole clouds, as in the bottom row, or a single whole cloud, as in the next row up, with half-clouds at the edges. Each quatrefoil cloud head comprises four leaf-shaped segments. An elbow-shaped "connecting cloud" descends from the bottom of each cloud head, turns to its proper right, and then attaches to the side of a cloud head in the row below; thus linked, the cloud heads form strong diagonal patterns. One undulating cloud wisp of elongated triangular form extends laterally from the side of each cloud head. Each undulating wisp appears immediately below one of the curved, connecting clouds. In those rows with two whole cloud heads, the cloud wisps point toward the proper left. In the alternating rows, they point toward the proper right. Woven with brightly colored yarns and gold-faced threads, tiny representations of the Eight Auspicious Emblems (*bajixiang*) embellish the clouds. Each leaf-shaped cloud segment and each undulating triangular wisp has one emblem, while each elbow-shaped connecting cloud boasts two motifs. In those rows with two whole cloud heads, each connecting cloud has one of the Eight Auspicious Emblems and a blossoming branch; in the alternating rows, each connecting cloud claims one auspicious emblem and a swastika—an auspicious Buddhist sign that in China not only symbolizes good fortune but serves as a stylized form of the ideograph *wan*, meaning "ten thousand." A ribbon with fluttering tails loops around each of the Eight Auspicious Emblems, distinguishing those emblems from the swastikas and flowering branches, which lack such marks. Each element of every cloud—from the leaf-shaped segments to the curving connectors to the undulating wisps—was brocaded in yarn of a different color, imparting a brilliant and varied effect to the finished fabric.[1] Although the decorative motifs repeat in alternating rows, the color combinations vary from cloud to cloud—within each row as well as from row to row. Because the fabric has been cut at the top and bottom and along the proper right side, it cannot be determined whether or not the color combinations were repeated in the original fabric. Double outlines enclose each colored area. The inner outlines are woven with silk yarn of contrasting color, typically a color from another element of the same cloud; the outer outlines are woven with gold-faced yarns. The selvage is present along the proper left edge. The foundation wefts are continuous across this textile; the colorful supplementary wefts begin where first needed in the design scheme and then continue across the width of the textile. On the obverse, the supplementary wefts appear only in the brocaded areas; on the reverse, they appear only in the undecorated areas. Unbound on the reverse, the supplementary wefts float in those areas where not required by the design scheme. The gold-faced supplementary wefts are flat strips of paper

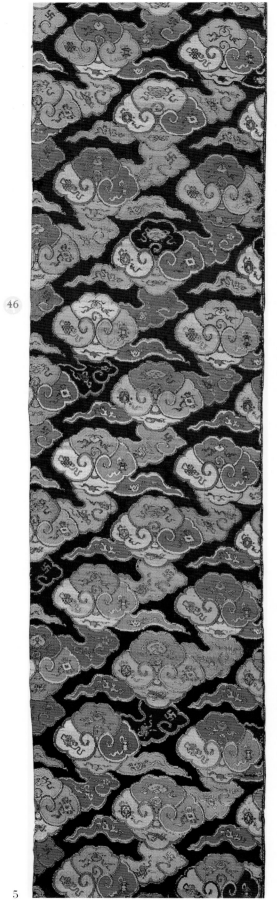

5

[Section]

5

[Detail]

to which gold leaf has been applied over a ground of bole on the obverse, the gold-embellished paper further adhered to a dark tan substrate yarn. Much of the gold leaf has been lost, exposing the underlying bole, which is dark rust red in color. The tip of each gold-faced supplementary weft is visible within the selvage that extends down the fabric's proper left edge; on first inspection, these gold-faced weft tips give the impression of a single, continuous, gold-faced, warp thread running vertically through the selvage. A recent addition, the blue cotton fabric with woven stripes that now lines the back of this textile conceals the floating wefts and protects them from snagging, pulling, and other damage.

The use for which this sumptuous textile was intended can not now be known. The luxury materials, including gold-faced threads, and the very tight weave suggest that the fabric might have been made for the imperial court; indeed, it is customarily said to be tribute silk. The excellent condition indicates that the textile was little used, further suggesting that this textile might have been presented to a Buddhist monastery in Tibet, where it might well have been stored until very recent times. Although they would make it appropriate for presentation to a Buddhist temple, the Eight Auspicious Emblems that ornament this textile do not necessarily indicate that it was made for religious use, as such Buddhist-derived symbols in fact were often used in secular contexts during the Ming and Qing periods.

47

Popular in Ming and Qing times, the *bajixiang*, or Eight Auspicious Emblems, motif was introduced to Chinese art from Tibetan Buddhism during the Yuan dynasty; it appears occasionally on Jingdezhen porcelains and Longquan celadons of the day.[2] Best known as an ornamental motif in the decorative arts, the Eight Auspicious Emblems were also fashioned independently as small sculptures in porcelain, gilt bronze, and cloisonné enamel for placement on Buddhist altars or in three-dimensional *mandalas* (cosmological diagrams).[3] Although they vary considerably in Yuan-dynasty depictions, both the emblems constituting the motif and their order of appearance had been standardized by Ming times as follows:

> Wheel (*lun*) symbolizing the Wheel of the Law (*falun*) and thus
> the Buddha and His teachings
> Conch Shell (*luo*) symbolizing majesty, felicitous travel, and the
> voice of the Buddha
> Canopy (*chuang*) symbolizing spiritual authority, reverence,
> and purity
> Umbrella (*san* or *gai*) symbolizing royal grace
> Flower (*hua*) symbolizing truth, purity, and creative power
> Vase or Jar (*ping*) symbolizing eternal harmony, abundant
> blessings, and ultimate triumph over birth and death
> Double Fish (*yu*) symbolizing fertility, abundance, conjugal
> happiness, and protection against evil
> Endless Knot (*jie*) symbolizing longevity, eternity, and receipt
> of the Buddha's assistance[4]

Too small to allow a detailed analysis of their style, the representations of the Eight Auspicious Emblems in this Clague collection textile nonetheless reflect a mid-Ming style: they are presented simply and directly, without elaborate backgrounds and without the vase- or lotus-blossom-shaped supports that soared to popularity in later periods. In addition, the ribbons that adorn the emblems are not only simple and restrained but are sometimes asymmetrically arranged, in contrast to the elaborate ribbons favored in Qing times, which tend to be symmetrically disposed.[5]

Perhaps the surest parallels that can be cited as stylistic evidence in dating this exquisite textile are the cloisonné enamels[6] and polychrome porcelains[7] that not only characterize Ming-dynasty taste but reflect its preference for a broad palette of bright and varied colors.[8] In particular, this brilliantly patterned textile finds aesthetic kinship in the enameled porcelains produced at Jingdezhen, Jiangxi province, during the Jiajing reign (1522–1566) of the Ming dynasty; that kinship is evident both in the range of colors and in their bold juxtapositions.[9] The results of a radiocarbon test conducted by Timothy Jull at The University of Arizona NSF-Arizona AMS Facility, Tucson, on a small sample removed from it confirm that this textile dates between the early fifteenth and mid-seventeenth centuries, a chronological range that is consistent with the mid- to late sixteenth-century attribution proposed here.[10]

[RDM]

Technical analysis

Warp: Dark marine blue silk; Z twist; single ply. Count: 46 yarns per centimeter. *Weft*: Foundation: 1) Dark navy blue silk; Z twist; single ply. 2) Dark navy blue silk (of much larger diameter than the previous fiber, but otherwise very similar); no apparent twist; single ply. Count: 13 pairs (including one yarn of each type treated as one yarn when woven) of foundation weft yarns per centimeter. Both yarns of the pair are in the same shed. The two types of foundation weft yarns are closely related, differing only in twist and diameter of yarn. Supplementary: 1) Polychrome silk; no apparent twist; single ply. Count: 13 yarns per centimeter. 2) A flat gold adhered to a dark tan substrate yarn; no twist; no ply. Count: 13 gold yarns per centimeter. Condition: Gold is missing from approximately one-third of the gilded yarns. In many localized areas, the gold yarns are broken in those areas where they show on the reverse. *Weave*: Ground fabric is four-end satin with supplementary wefts in a brocade weave. Other: Brocade is the binding of the two types of supplementary wefts. On the obverse, the gold wefts are bound by the warps in a 1/7 tabby weave; on the reverse, the supplementary wefts are unbound. Most of the silk supplementary wefts begin where first needed in the pattern and extend across the width of the textile; other colors are inserted only in the small areas where they are required for the pattern. The gold yarns begin at each motif, pass for a short distance on the reverse (in areas where not needed in the pattern on the obverse), and then end on the far side of the motif. Condition: Each end of the textile has some small areas of broken yarns; the damaged areas have been stabilized. *Dyeing*: Yarn dyed. *Selvages*: One selvage is present. Weave: Tabby. Width: 0.4 centimeter. Location: The selvage runs the entire length of the textile's proper left edge—that is, along the edge that appears navy blue for its entire length.

Lining

The present lining is not original to the textile; the lining is a woven, striped, blue, cotton fabric.

Commentary

Long, thread-relief lines appear on the surface of this textile, running parallel to the warp yarns. The lines are not rows of machine stitches, as might be suspected; rather, they are integral to the original weaving. In all probability, the lines result from a particular warp yarn that is a little larger in diameter than those surrounding it, causing it to stand out and thus to be very noticeable to the viewer.

[MWG]

1   The numerous colors include white, celadon green, olive green, medium green, forest green, canary yellow, golden yellow, pale pink, rose pink, salmon, lavender, azure, midnight blue, and brown.

2   See Zhou 1987, p. 321, no. 3; p. 323, no. 18; p. 324, nos. 19-21; San Francisco 1983, p. 50, color pl. 30.

3   See Phoenix 1980, p. 111, no. 48; Rhie, Thurman, and Bigelow 1991, pp. 280-281, no. 103; pp. 338-340, no. 134; p. 382, no. 159; Zhou 1987, p. 329, no. 46.

4   Phoenix 1993, p. 109, no. 20; Zhou 1987, pp. 314-316; New York 1989, fig. 73; San Francisco 1983, p. 171, no. 111.

5   For a Wanli-period (1572-1620) porcelain bowl with overglaze enamel decoration representing the Eight Auspicious Emblems adorned with simple ribbons akin to those on this Clague collection textile, see Wang 1999, p. 205, no. 187.

6   See Phoenix 1980; New York 1989.

7   See Fujioka and Hasebe 1976.

8   For a discussion of the Ming taste for an expanding palette of bright colors, see Cambridge 1997, pp. 33-34.

9   See Wang 1999, p. 16, no. 15; Hasebe 1973, n.p., no. 87; Fujioka and Hasebe 1976, pp. 74-75, nos. 75-76.

10 Sample date number: AA-31550. According to Timothy Jull, on the basis of the radiocarbon tests, this textile can be assigned to the period 1441-1636 with sixty eight per cent confidence or to the period 1417-1658 with ninety five per cent confidence.
    Letter dated 23 February 1999 from A. J. T. Jull, The University of Arizona NSF-Arizona AMS Facility, Tucson, to Claudia Brown, Research Curator for Asian Art, Phoenix Art Museum.

6 Ceremonial Shawl with Horizontal Stripes, Tibetan Buddhist Inscriptions and Eight Auspicious Emblems (*Bajixiang*)

Ming dynasty, 15th–16th century
   Silk tabby with supplementary wefts; polychrome silk yarns in counterchanged weave
H. 204.5 cm (without fringe); W. 51 cm, including selvages

This textile was made using a remarkable and painstaking variation of tabby weave with supplementary wefts.[1] Employing a weaving technique called counterchanging (see technical analysis below), the weavers manipulated very fine-gauge colored yarns to create a cloth that is double-faced and reversible in the sense that no loose threads dangle on the reverse and hence the fabric appears finished on both sides. The colors include red, blue, green, yellow, white, and tan. 49

The decorative program is conceived in vertical symmetry. A white silk band appears at the top and bottom. Working inward, the weaver has created bright colored bands and then a lattice-like border. The latter can be interpreted as interlocking *wan* (swastikas; see number 5) in blue against a red ground. More bright colored bands—a pattern of three narrow and one broad stripe, repeated three times—are then followed by two-line inscriptions in Tibetan script. Another series of colored bands follows and then in two registers the *bajixiang* (see number 5), Eight Auspicious Emblems, appear, each with a lotus blossom just below. Examining the registers from top to bottom, these are woven in green against a white ground, yellow against a green ground, then green against white, and red against green. The colors appear in reverse on the back of the shawl. In a similar sequence, the lotus blossoms appear yellow against tan, green against white, yellow against tan, and blue against white. Another set of bright colored stripes borders the *bajixiang*. The central and largest field of the textile is given over to one large Sanskrit-derived symbol, woven in blue against a red ground. The motif is itself enshrined with a flaming mandorla and a lotiform base, as if the weavers were picturing a free-standing votive image.

The central image is the Tibetan motif called the *kalacakra*. This symbol is formed of ten interlocking syllables (including *Om Ham Ksha Ma La Va Ra Ya Sva Ha*) called the "all-powerful ten," written in Lantsa characters, an Indic script derived from Sanskrit and used for Buddhist devotional inscriptions. Together these syllables form both a mantra and a cosmological diagram.[2] The *kalacakra* emblem appears in more elaborate form in Qing textiles, depicted as here with a lotiform base but with added embellishments of floral, cloud and other motifs.[3]

The *bajixiang* motifs, discussed at length in the previous entry, are arranged left to right, the wheel, the umbrella, the endless knot, the conch shell, the flower, the vase, the double fish, and the canopy. Their placement is the same in both occurrences, although the colors differ. Similarly the inscriptions at either end repeat the same short text in different colors. The verses are in Tibetan and may be rendered:

> Happiness in the daytime, happiness at night,
> Happiness at midday,
> Day or night, always happiness,
> May the blessings of the precious Three Jewels [Buddha, Dharma, Sangha] be [ever] present!
> [translation by Jane Gregorie]

The full text is repeated at each end of the shawl. The phrase "Three Jewels" refers to the Buddha, the Dharma (his teaching), and the Sangha (the Buddhist community). The same poem appears on ceramics of the Xuande reign (1426–1435)[4] and on textiles commissioned by the Qianlong emperor (r. 1736–1795).[5]

This shawl was made for Buddhist ceremonial purposes, probably for use as a *kata*, or offering scarf; its double-faced weave and its long fringe are clearly related to that function. The *kata* is used even today in making Buddhist offerings; often the supplicant makes a gift to a lama including the scarf and receives the blessed *kata* back in exchange. Offering scarves can also be "given" to Buddhist images by devotees who place the cloth on the image itself. These may remain draped over the hands of a Buddha or Bodhisattva.[6]

Stylistic links to other textiles as well as ceramics and metalwork of the Ming dynasty can be found in the representations of the *bajixiang*. More elaborate than those of the textile in the previous entry, the emblems shown here are adorned with stylized ribbons and have lotus flowers positioned as supports for each symbol. A similar concept can be seen in cloisonné enamels of the sixteenth century;[7] the lotus blossoms are simplified and placed below each emblem, but they still function as separate motifs and are not elaborated into pedestals. Based on these stylistic considerations, this offering scarf can be dated to the fifteenth to sixteenth century.[8]

[CB]

6

6

[Detail: front]

6

[Detail: back]

Technical analysis

Warp: Off-white silk; no twist; no ply (bundled yarns not twisted together). Count: 30 yarns per centimeter. Yarns have a very thin diameter. When the warps are not being used to hold supplementary weft yarns, they float on the reverse side making that area appear "more white" in color. *Weft*: Foundation: Polychrome silk; no twist; no ply (bundled yarns not twisted together). Count: 14 to 18 yarns per centimeter. Other: Much thicker diameter yarns than the warp. Some areas have much thicker diameter weft yarns (could be called a slub) than the rest of the textile. Supplementary: Polychrome silk, no twist; no ply (bundled yarns not twisted together). Count: 14 to 18 yarns per centimeter. Other: Supplementary weft yarns have characteristics identical to the foundation weft yarns. A continuous supplementary weft appears only in the 15 horizontal stripes with a woven design. *Weave*: Tabby. It also has continuous supplementary wefts in a counterchanged extra weft float weave, that is, the color change is created by counterchanging a supplementary structure for area patterning. A weave structure is literally turned over and used now one face up, now the other (see Emery, 1980, p. 170). Other: There are many weaving mistakes throughout the textile. *Dyeing*: Yarn dyed. *Selvages*: Weave: Tabby. The last twelve warps on each selvage were created by bunching many warps into a thicker diameter warp and then weaving. Width: 2 centimeters. Location: Both sides. Other: There are two vertical stripes on each selvage. They are created by having the warps float over wefts exposing the off-white warps creating an off-white vertical stripe.

Fringe

The warp extends into long fringe (19 centimeters in length) at each end of the textile. The fringes are in poor condition as they are matted, broken and worn.

[MWG]

1 The Chinese term for this is *huajuan*, see Zhao 1999, pp. 337–339; Zhao also describes double-faced tabby (*shuangmianjuan*) which as here produces the same pattern but alternated colors on the two sides of the fabric.

2 For a modern interpretation of the *kalacakra* symbolism, see Beer 1999, pp. 123–127.

3 See, for example, an embroidered *kalacakra* of Qing date, Huang 1985, cat. no. 205.

4 For a Xuande period porcelain stembowl with this Tibetan poem inscribed in underglaze blue, see Valenstein 1989, plate 151 and page 165.

5 Cited by Bartholomew 1991, who illustrates one of the Qianlong textiles, and gives a slightly different rendering of the poem. Patricia Berger, offering yet another translation of the same poem, cites its use on "prayer scarves woven during the Qianlong period as greeting gifts for Tibetan lamas." See her cat. no. 13, p. 255 in Lawrence, KS 1994.

6 For a twentieth century photograph documenting the practice, see Tung 1980, plate 26.

7 For example, New York 1989, cat. no. 80.

8 In a personal communication to Claudia Brown, 21 August 2000, Terese Bartholomew confirmed that this polychrome scarf differs from the Qianlong period ones. The latter are woven in white only or in other solid colors, and their presentation of the *bajixiang* differs significantly from this example in the Clague collection.

7   Large Square Panel with Crossed *Vajras*, Eight Auspicious Emblems
     (*Bajixiang*), Lotus Blossoms and other Buddhist Symbols

Ming to early Qing dynasty, 17th–18th century
    Silk lampas; red silk ground of dyed yarns in 2/1 twill weave, interwoven in tabby
    weave with gold-colored silk yarns
H. 92 cm, including fringe; W. 92 cm, including selvages

Woven in a technique known as lampas,[1] which involves adding motifs in a patterning weft   53
bound by extra warp yarns to a foundation weave, this cloth presents a richly and densely
embellished surface of gold-colored patterns against a red ground. The central motif of the textile
is conceived as a large eight-petaled lotus blossom. At its center are the crossed *vajras* with
their curving prongs. Emanating from the center are the Eight Auspicious Emblems (*bajixiang*),
each within a petal of the lotus. A second set of eight petals is shown as if partially visible
behind the first. Arranged around the perimeter are stylized lotus blossoms, with scrolling
foliage. A square border of lotus scrolls encloses the composition. Perhaps to adapt the scrolling
pattern to the square shape, a vase is added for the blossoms in the four corners.

This textile is perfectly square including its selvages and fringes, and thus appears to be complete
as originally woven. Its shape and its radial symmetry suggest that the textile was intended for
use as a canopy, suspended to be seen from below, rather than as a wall hanging. A recently
published textile of similar color and radial organization,[2] bears the inscription in Sanskrit,
"Om mani padme hum" (see number 3). The two textiles are close enough in technique to have
been made in the same workshop, despite slight differences in style, and for use in similar contexts
within the practice of Buddhist devotion.

The symbol of the *vajra*, also called a thunderbolt, is emblematic of the power of knowledge
over ignorance. The term *vajra* is associated with the hardness of the diamond and thus the
enduring and indestructible nature of Buddhist teaching or enlightenment. The Tantric Buddhism
practiced in Tibet is often called Vajrayana or the Diamond Vehicle. The form of the *vajra*
varies, but it is usually depicted two-dimensionally as a hand-held symbolic weapon with three
prongs at either end. Sometimes the center portion of the *vajra* incorporates stylized lotus blossom
motifs and the prongs themselves often emanate from the mouths of *makaras* (see number 4).
The weavers of this textile alluded to these shapes in their depictions of the implements. The
crossed *vajra* (*vishvavajra*) fuses two *vajra* shapes into a wheel-like motif with additional cosmic
implications, suggesting both the power and the stability of the universe.[3] The Eight Auspicious
Emblems (*bajixiang*, discussed fully in number 5) are associated with virtues and good wishes.
The lotus, symbolic of purity and innate reason, is a frequent decorative complement to
Buddhist imagery in the Ming and Qing periods.

The radial organization of the motifs may have sources in the decoration of the upper surfaces of round boxes of the early Ming period.[4] Notably a fifteenth century carved lacquer box in the collection of the Seattle Art Museum has similar motifs: an eight-petaled lotus flower in the center and the *bajixiang* motifs on lotus supports disposed radially around the perimeter.[5] Another close link is found in works of the *qiangjin* (engraved gold) lacquer technique that features gold patterns against a red ground. The technique appears in Buddhist sutra covers dated to 1410 as well as in a later group commissioned by the Qianlong emperor.[6] The early Ming dynasty mantra in the Clague collection (number 3) employs this palette of gold on a red ground using gilt strips of paper. In this example, the solemn and elegant effect of red and gold is created by the use of pale yellowish white yarns as a pattern weft within the deep red ground.

[CB]

Technical analysis

Warp: Rust red silk; Z twist; single ply. Count: 144 yarns per centimeter, including the binding warp. Step: Two main warps. Condition: Photochemical damage; a few breaks caused by nails. Binding: Same as foundation warp. *Weft*: Foundation: Rust red silk, Z twist, single ply. Count: 21 passes per centimeter. Pass: Two main wefts and one supplementary weft. Step: One pass. Supplementary: (Pattern weft) pale gold-colored silk; no apparent twist; single ply. Count: 21 supplementary weft yarns per centimeter. Other: Supplementary wefts are added in a tabby weave. *Weave*: Lampas. Foundation weave: 2/1 Z twill. Supplementary weave: Tabby. Condition: Previously the two ends of the textile had been turned under and hemmed with a sewing machine; these were recently removed in conservation. *Dyeing*: Yarn dyed. *Selvages*: The selvage warps are a yellow yarn of large diameter. They are thicker than the other warp yarns, have a Z twist, 2 ply. Weave: Tabby. Width: 1 centimeter. Location: On both sides so the finished woven width of the textile is 92 centimeters. Other: Weft yarns turn around the outermost warp. Condition: Small cuts have been made in the outermost warp yarns.

Commentary

Definitions of lampas and pattern weft follow Burnham 1980, pp. 82 and 98.

[MWG]

1   For a full description of lampas (*tejiejin*), see Zhao 1999, p. 341.

2   Spink 1994, cat. no. 17. Here a mantra of Sanskrit characters reads in a circular fashion around the central motif. The textile is smaller than the present example, and lacks selvages; perhaps it has been cut down by the width of a square border now lost.

3   For an illustration and discussion of a ceremonial *vajra*, see Pal 1983, pp. 242–243. For a three-dimensional representation of the crossed *vajra*, see National Palace Museum 1971, cat. no. 31. On the contemporary interpretation of the crossed *vajra* in Tibetan Buddhist practice, see Beer 1999, pp. 239–243.

4   See for example, New York 1989, cat. nos. 2–4; and related dishes, cat. nos. 10 and 14.

5   Garner 1979, plate 39.

6   Examples of both are illustrated and discussed in Berger and Bartholomew 1995, pp. 188–189, cat. no. 47 and fig. 1.

8
[Front]

8
[Back]

Qing dynasty, probably 18–19th century, construction, employing Ming and Qing, probably 17–18th century, fabrics

> Silk damask brocaded with supplementary wefts; yellow silk ground of dyed yarns in 3/1 broken twill weave, the ground interwoven in brocade weave with polychrome silk yarns, with gold-wrapped yarns, and with flat gold leaf adhered to paper substrate
> H. 146 cm; W. 197 cm

Sixty-five fragments of three different fabrics are stitched together to form the garment. The upper part is formed by fabric woven in damask with brocade patterns interwoven in the quatrefoil shape called a cloud collar, including two large motifs of four-clawed *mang* dragons (as opposed to the *long* typically shown at this time with five claws; see number 2). A seam runs vertically down the center of the back and front joining two halves of the dragon-and-pearl motif. In each case the seam runs between the two large eyes of the *mang* dragon. The sleeves have been extended using pieces of fabrics woven with the same characteristics, including the damask fabric with cloud patterns identical to the damask ground of the central section and a brocade fabric identical in technical characteristics to the large brocaded area. These brocade sections represent smaller, profile *mang* pursuing or grasping flaming pearls (see number 2) with waves beneath and clouds above. Just above the waves the weaver has included symbols of the *bajixiang*, Eight Auspicious Emblems (see number 5). The lower section of both front and back is composed of three long rectangles of fabric similar to that used in extending the sleeves. The sides of the garment are then pieced together to form the pronounced flaring profile. Some of the pieces, including triangular and trapezoidal shapes, are from fabrics woven with characteristics distinct from the two types previously mentioned. Although the motif of the profile, four-clawed *mang* dragon, with waves below and clouds above, is similar, the style and proportions of the motifs differ as do the colors incorporated into the brocade. This fabric is woven with a narrower range of colors and with less complexity in the representations of the *mang*, the mountains and waves, and the clouds. Colors included here are two shades of blue, two shades of green, red, and black, whereas in the fabrics of the main part of the garment, this palette is extended to include pink. It is, however, not so much the number of colors but the use of them that gives the different appearance. For example, in the dragons of these small pieces at the side of the skirt, the spine of each dragon is a series of tooth-like projections in white threads and the underside of the dragon is a rhythmically broken line of dark blue. However, in the dragons of the large rectangular sections, the spines alternate white and blue, and the underside is accented with shades red, green, black, and blue. Likewise the other motifs display a difference of color and complexity.

This robe is of the Tibetan type called a *chuba*. Distinguished by its tapering sleeves and its profile which flares outward toward the hem, the *chuba* can range from a practical to a ceremonial garment. The more elaborate *chuba* were often made out of silk yardage woven in China and many such examples survive in museum and private collections.[1] Silks and other textiles were regularly traded by the Chinese for Tibetan horses and also presented as gifts to Tibetan

Buddhist lamas. The practice began before the Ming dynasty and continued throughout the Ming and Qing periods.[2] As in other border areas, robes were also dispensed together with rank and privilege to leaders with allegiance to the Chinese court. Silk for court robes, and the privilege to wear dragon robes, were bestowed on Tibetan nobles and high lamas, and on Mongol nobles and high ranking military leaders.[3] The Clague *chuba* is similar to robes worn by Tibetan officials on ceremonial occasions and documented in twentieth-century photographs.[4]

The material from which this *chuba* was constructed is of the type that became standard in the late Ming period. The cloud-patterned damask, for example, is similar to a standard Ming type known in excavated examples.[5] Moreover, the four lobed cloud collar brocaded into the damask is also a well documented Late Ming type, including examples excavated from the tomb of the Wanli emperor (reigned 1573–1620).[6] In these and related examples,[7] two dragons (in the imperial case) or two *mang* (for civil and military officials) stretch from one lobe to the next, intended to cross over the shoulders to the front and the back of the finished robe. The width of the standard loom apparently dictated the need for a seam which typically runs vertically between the eyes of the two dragons. The yardages also include running (five-clawed) dragons or (four-clawed) *mang* organized in pairs and intended to adorn the skirt of a finished robe.[8] As noted by several scholars, this type of robe continued to be made in the Qing dynasty.[9]

An interesting parallel to the construction of the *chuba* from Chinese silks of this type is the making of Buddhist patchwork garments. For example, a *kesa*, or Buddhist priest's mantle, now in the collection of the Victoria and Albert Museum,[10] was sewn in Japan using portions of damask and brocade very similar to the fabric of this *chuba* except red rather than yellow in ground color. The lobed collar and damask areas were cut into rectangles and repositioned to make a large rectangle with eighteen running *mang* pieced together to form a continuous border. The patchwork of the mantle has symbolic implications reflecting the Buddha's vow of poverty, and while this would not be so overt a reference in the *chuba* there certainly is in Tibet's Buddhist tradition a sense of nobility in patchwork construction. The construction of the *kesa*, however, seems deliberately to avoid inverting any of the dragon fragments, whereas the *chuba* includes several inverted dragon patterns which would have been visible when the garment was worn.

Dating the fabrics of the Clague *chuba* is made difficult by the continuation of this tradition over so long a period. However, the older side panels of the garment (see detail, bottom of page 61) are so close in style to examples of the Wanli period that they may be dated to the late sixteenth to early seventeenth century. The later fabric appearing throughout the main body of the robe has stylistic complexities that may better be attributed to the late seventeenth or eighteenth century.[11]

[CB]

Publications: Claudia Brown, "The Amy S. Clague Collection of Chinese Textiles," *Orientations* 31, no. 2 (February 2000), p. 35, fig. 11.

8
[Detail]

Technical analysis

Sixty-five pieces of fabric are stitched together to make the robe and there are three different fabrics in the robe. Two of these could have been made as a set as the fabrics' colors, thread count, ways of creating gold threads and technique of creating supplemental weft designs are identical. The third has a slightly different ground color, a different gold wrapped thread and lower thread count; there are also subtle differences in the pattern.

Fabric 1

Dark yellow damask fabric. Location: Bottom layer of robe front and section of sides of skirt, also top of robe where it has a very large dragon medallion woven in brocade in the center of the damask fabric (a section of one medallion has a seam between it and the damask fabric). *Warp*: Yellow silk; no twist; single ply. Count: 40 yarns per centimeter. Other: Very fine yarns. *Weft*: There is one type of polychrome supplementary weft yarn and two different gold supplementary weft yarns found in the large dragon medallion. Foundation: Yellow silk; S twist; single ply. Count: 26 yarns per centimeter. Other: Wefts are much larger diameter yarns than warp yarns. Supplementary: 1) Polychrome silk; no twist; single ply. Count: 12 yarns per centimeter. Other: Large diameter yarns. On the reverse side of brocaded areas, the wefts float. The weft forms loops while turning into the next shed. 2) Core yarns: orange silk; no twist; no ply (bundled yarns not twisted together); wrapping of gold leaf adhered to off-white substrate, Z twist. Other: On the reverse side of brocaded areas, the wefts float. The weft forms loops while turning into the next shed. Count: 10 pairs of yarn per centimeter. Pairs of gold wrapped yarns are treated as one when woven. 3) strips of gold leaf adhered to a flat off-white substrate. Gilded on one side. Count: 10 yarns per centimeter. Other: This strip usually appears as a short yarn without other yarns like it in its vicinity. Condition: fifty percent of the yarns have lost their gold leaf. *Weave*: Damask. Background is a 3/1 broken twill weave. *Dyeing*: Yarn dyed. *Selvages*: None remaining.

Fabric 2

Location: in the skirt and sleeves of robe. *Warp*: Yellow silk; Z twist; single ply. Count: 40 yarns per centimeter. Other: Small diameter. *Weft*: There is one type of polychrome supplementary silk yarn and two different gold supplementary weft yarns. Foundation: Gold-colored silk, slight S twist; 3-ply, S. Count: 26 yarns per centimeter. Other: Weft yarns are much larger diameter than warp yarns. Supplementary: 1) Polychrome silk; no twist; single ply. Count: 12 yarns per centimeter. Other: On the reverse side of brocaded areas, the wefts float. The weft forms loops while turning into the next shed. 2) Core yarns: orange silk; no twist; no ply (bundled yarns not twisted together). Wrapping: Gold leaf adhered to off-white substrate, Z twist. Count: 20 yarns per centimeter. Pairs of gold wrapped yarns are treated as one when woven. Other: On the reverse side of brocaded areas, the wefts float. The weft forms loops while turning into the next shed. 3) Strip of gold leaf adhered to a flat off-white substrate. Count: 10 yarns per centimeter. Other: This strip usually appears as a short yarn without other like yarns near it. Condition: fifty percent of the yarns have lost their gold leaf. *Weave*: Brocade - the background weave is a 3/1 broken twill. *Dyeing*: Yarn dyed. *Selvages*: Weave: Tabby. Width: 1 centimeter. Location: On some seam allowances hidden from view. Other: The warp and weft yarns are bundled together and then woven in the tabby weave. Warp Count: 12 yarns per centimeter. Weft Count: 15 yarns per centimeter.

Fabric 3

Location: sides of robe's skirt. *Warp*: yellow silk; Z twist; single ply. Count: 29 yarns per centimeter. *Weft*: There is one type of polychrome silk supplementary weft yarn and two different gold supplementary weft yarns. Foundation: Yellow silk; S twist; two yarns, not twisted together. Count: 24 yarns per centimeter. Supplementary: 1) Polychrome silk; no twist; single ply. Count: 10 yarns per centimeter. Other: On the reverse side of brocaded areas, the wefts float. The weft forms loops while turning into the next shed. 2) Core yarns: Pale yellow silk; no twist; no ply (bundled yarns not twisted together). Wrapping: gold leaf adhered to off-white substrate, Z twist. Count: 20 yarns per centimeter. Pairs of the gold wrapped yarns are treated as one when woven. Other: On the reverse side of brocaded areas, the wefts float. The weft forms loops while turning into the next shed. 3) Strip of gold leaf adhered to a flat off-white substrate. Count: 10 yarns per centimeter. Other: This strip usually appears as a short yarn without other like yarns near it. Condition: seventy percent of the yarns have lost their gold leaf. *Weave*: Brocade background weave is a broken 3/1 twill. Condition: yarn pulls on the surface; soiling. *Dyeing*: Yarn dyed. *Selvages*: none visible.

Lining

The lining is taupe color tabby weave silk fabric, probably a replacement. The red facings are a silk damask weave fabric and were attached to the robe with machine stitches suggesting a date for this adaptation after the invention of the sewing machine in the 1850s.

[MWG]

8

[Detail]

[Detail]

1 Toronto 1996, cat. no. 118; Mailey, p. 15; Hong Kong 1995,
  cat. nos. 53, 55, 56, 57 and 64.

2 Sperling 1979, describes this exchange.

3 Rawski 1998, pp. 42–43. For specific examples of how Manchu
  emperors bestowed specific favors, including gifts of robes as well as
  whole cloth, see Berger and Bartholomew 1995, pp. 138–141.

4 Tung 1980, pl. 108; the officials are described as wearing replicas of
  robes worn by 17th century Mongol generals. See also Richardson
  1993, p. 31, where a ceremonial commander (appointed with the
  Mongol title of Yaso) is pictured wearing a similar robe.

5 See Zhao 2000, p. 48 and figs. 7 and 8.

6 Huang 1987, cat. nos. 31, 32, and 34.

7 Zhao 1999, pp. 278–279, cat. no. 09.05. A related example in
  embroidered velvet is illustrated by Vollmer 1977, pp. 40–41.

8 For an example of a finished Chinese robe of the type,
  see Hong Kong 1995, cat. no. 58.

9 See Hong Kong 1995, cat. no. 58; for an early Qing example,
  see Garrett 1998, pl. 3.

10 Verity Wilson (Wilson 1986, p. 117–118) argues for a Ming date
   for the red robe silk.

11 Since the Mongols were brought under Qing control in 1661 and
   adopted the Manchu dress code at that time, it is tempting to link
   this type of dress with that date (see note 4 above).

Qing dynasty, probably late 18th–19th century
  Silk brocade; salmon (faded from medium orange or red) silk ground of dyed yarns in
  2/1 twill weave, the ground interwoven in brocade weave with polychrome silk yarns,
  with gold-wrapped yarns, and with flat gold leaf adhered to paper substrate
H. 165.6 cm; W. 52.8 cm

Designed as a chair cover, this long, vertically oriented, rectangular, silk textile is divided into four compositional sections, each intended to cover a different part of the chair. A framed rectangular panel at the top would have been draped over the top of the chair to anchor the textile and to ornament the chair's rear face (this panel, with its pair of flying cranes, appears upside down when the textile is displayed vertically). A square section featuring a dragon-and-pearl motif surrounded by scrolling clouds would have embellished the chair's back splat. Another cloud-bordered, square area with a formalized medallion of stylized dragons, birds, and blossoms would have adorned the chair's seat (the horizontal lines of damage at the top and bottom of this area indicate that this cover was actually used, just as they indicate the exact points at which it was folded to fit the chair seat). Finally, a framed rectangular panel at the bottom would have hung from the front edge of the seat, concealing the open area below.

Brocaded entirely with colored silk yarns on the salmon ground, the framed panel at the top features two white cranes with navy blue markings that fly to either side of a triangular blue-and-green mountain rising from the rolling waves at the bottom of the scene. Perforated rocks flanking the crystalline mountain push through the whitecaps of the blue and green waves. The symmetrically disposed cranes face each other, each bearing a sprig of auspicious *lingzhi* fungus in its beak. Variegated cloud scrolls complete the scene. Woven with gold-wrapped yarns, the four-clawed dragon that dominates the area below the crane panel is the principal focus of this textile, as it would have been the most visible decorative element when the cover was draped over the chair. Horned, whiskered, and maned, the dragon coils about a pearl, looking directly out at the viewer; surrounded by multicolored clouds, the dragon floats in the heavens, above a triangular mountain that rises from whitecapped waves of blue and green. A pair of stylized, navy blue dragons loops through a dotted green ring, recalling a beaded jade disc, at each corner of the formalized medallion that embellishes that section of the textile that covered the chair's seat. Each of the tail-to-tail paired dragons faces its counterpart at the adjacent corner, looking across the pair of confronting, crested birds that forms each of the medallion's sides. A large composite blossom, brocaded in sky blue silk and gold-wrapped yarns and reminiscent of an Islamic floral arabesque, occupies the center of the medallion; four navy blue *taotie* masks surround the composite blossom, each mask with white fangs, pink eyes, and green eyebrows. The boughs of green foliage that anchor the central floral motif to the corner dragons frame small flowers or sprigs of *lingzhi* fungus. Variegated clouds fill the spaces outside the medallion. The lowermost section of the textile, which would have hung below the chair's seat, boasts a framed panel with a pair of confronting, four-clawed dragons. Woven with gold-faced threads and presented in profile, the dragons reach for the flaming pearl (resembling a sun or moon) that hovers in the cloud-dotted sky above the triangular mountain rising from the rolling, whitecapped sea of blue and green at the bottom of the composition. A narrow band of interlaced dragons with foliate bodies borders the textile on all four sides. Although each section features a discrete design scheme, the scrolling clouds and the shared border and color scheme impart a visual unity to the textile. Except for the principal dragon, every element of this textile is symmetrically arranged in terms of both colors and design elements. Outlines of contrasting color enclose most colored areas, excluding some of the white areas.

Careful examination of individual threads within the weave reveals that the silk ground originally was medium orange or red, the present salmon hue resulting from fading. Both selvages are present; because they have been folded under the textile, they are not visible on the obverse. The foundation wefts are continuous across this textile; the colorful supplementary silk wefts begin where first needed in the design scheme and then continue across the width of the textile. On the obverse, the supplementary silk wefts appear only in the brocaded areas; on the reverse, they appear only in the undecorated areas. The gold-faced supplementary wefts are discontinuous, appearing only in those limited, localized areas where required by the design scheme. This textile employs two different types of gold-faced supplementary wefts: those used for the principal dragon and for the composite blossom in the formalized medallion might be termed "wrapped" threads, as each has a bundled core of pale yellow silk fibers around which is wrapped a narrow strip of paper whose outer face has been embellished with gold leaf over a ground of bole;[1] those used for the pair of dragons in the textile's lowermost section are flat strips of tan paper to which gold leaf has been adhered over a ground of bole. Most of the gold leaf is still present in those wrapped threads used for the medallion, so the composite blossom appears lustrous and golden. By contrast, much of the gold has disappeared from the wrapped threads used for the principal dragon and from the flat strips of tan paper used for the pair of dragons at the bottom, exposing the copper colored bole. Although a first, quick inspection might suggest that the dragons were brocaded with red-gold-faced threads—or even with copper-faced threads—in fact, the dragons were worked with yellow-gold-faced threads; thus, the dragons originally were lustrous and golden, their present copper color an accident resulting from loss of gold leaf.

Chinese paintings and woodblock-printed images reveal that the Chinese had begun to drape chairs with long narrow panels of fabric by the Ming dynasty, at least in formal settings.[2] Such covers typically were made in pairs, just as the hardwood chairs they covered were made in pairs.[3] In some instances, a table might be draped with a matching frontal (compare number 4), so that a grouping of furniture could be harmonized with a covering common to the set.[4] In discussing such chair covers, Myrna Myers has commented:

> It is essential to underline the importance of textiles produced for predetermined functions during the Ming and Qing dynasties, like chair covers, table frontals and cushion covers, in contrast with textiles made up of yardage sewn into particular shapes. In the former case, in making the textile, the artisan had to foresee the elements which were to be used and was obliged to dispose the decorative elements according to a desired scheme. This organization at the outset could either harmonize with or underline the ultimate use of the piece or transmit a symbolic message, as in the chair strips which often had protective animals on the back section and floral motifs on the seat.[5]

The symbolism of the dragon paired with the flaming jewel, or pearl, remains the same as that stated in previous entries (see discussion number 2). Traditionally regarded as the bestower of life-sustaining water, the dragon was emblematically paired with clouds or with rolling waves from the Song dynasty onward. In Ming and Qing times, dragon imagery typically assumes cosmological symbolism. In this chair cover, for example, the dragon—the prime emblem of the *yang*, or male, forces of the universe—also symbolizes the heavens and cosmic forces in general; rising from the primordial seas, the triangular mountain peak over which the dragon appears represents the earth. Inspired by designs on works of art from China's Great Bronze Age (sixteenth century B.C.–A.D. 220), the taotie masks, birds, and ornamental, jadelike rings add an archaistic flavor to this textile. The appearance of both golden dragons and white cranes suggests that this cover must have been made for an official's chair, perhaps that of a palace official, though not for the emperor himself, as the dragon has but four claws rather than the imperial five.

Chair covers with four distinct compositional sections seem to have evolved in the eighteenth century. The central dragon's proportionally large head, its ovoid shape, and its very prominent forehead all point to a late eighteenth or nineteenth century date of manufacture for this cover. In addition, the style of the framed panels at its top and bottom recall that of badges of official rank used in the late eighteenth and nineteenth centuries. Closely related in size, coloration, style, and four-part organization, a chair cover in the collection of the Association pour l'Étude et la Documentation des Textiles d'Asie, Paris, has been attributed to the nineteenth century.[6] The central dragon panel of the salmon-hued AEDTA cover shows a marked resemblance to that of the Clague piece, suggesting that the two textiles might have been made by the same workshop at approximately the same time.

[RDM]

Technical analysis

Warp: Orange (faded from red) silk; slight Z twist; single ply. Count: 28 yarns per centimeter. Other: Very fine yarn diameter. Condition: faded and actively deteriorating. *Weft*: Foundation: Orange (faded from red) silk; no twist; no ply (bundled yarns not twisted together). Count: 17 yarns per centimeter. Supplementary: There are three types of supplementary weft yarns. 1) Polychrome silk; no twist; ply is a bundle of fibers. Count: 17 per centimeter. Location: Throughout textile. Condition: Good. 2) Bundle of pale yellow silk fibers around which has been wrapped a narrow strip of off-white substrate, probably paper, to which gold leaf has been adhered on the obverse over a ground of bole; Z twist. Dark pink bole is present on the metallic yarns in the medallion but seems to be absent in the metallic yarns used for the dragon. Count: 32 yarns per centimeter. Though double yarns, the gold-wrapped yarns are treated as single yarns when woven. Location: In the small central medallion and in the large dragon in the upper portion of the textile. Condition: The small medallion has bright, lustrous yarns; the metallic yarns in the large dragon are tarnished and have lost approximately thirty per cent of their gilding. 3) A strip of gold leaf adhered to a flat paper substrate, tan in color. Count: 15 yarns per centimeter. Location: On the two dragons at the bottom of the textile. Condition: The yarns are tarnished and have lost approximately fifty per cent of their gilding. *Weave*: Brocade. Fabric is a 2/1 twill weave. Condition: The warp yarns are actively deteriorating. Three localized areas show horizontal lines of damage resulting from broken warp threads; the damage probably resulted from the folding of the textile over edges when it was used as a chair cover. *Dyeing*: Yarn dyed. *Selvages*: Both selvages are present. Weave: 2/1 twill. Width: 0.5 centimeter. Selvage warps are white in color and thicker than the warps in the body of the textile. Condition: Horizontal clips have been cut in the selvages, perhaps to make the textile lie flat.

Lining

The present lining is not original to the textile.

Commentary

This textile was conserved in January 1996; at that time, a silk support fabric, taupe in color, was inserted between the textile and its lining. The conservation stitches are stitched to the textile and to this support fabric.

[MWG]

1   For information on gold-wrapped threads, see Tímár-Balázsy and Eastop 1998, esp. pp. 128–131.

2   For late Ming woodblock-printed book illustrations that include images of chairs covered with silk panels, see Machida 1988, p. 115, no. 26; p. 143, no. 90; p. 159, no. 19; p. 160, no. 23. For an early or mid-Ming yoke-back armchair draped with an eighteenth-century velvet cover, see Ellsworth 1997, p. 84, pl. 24.

3   For a Chongzhen-period (1628–1644) woodblock-printed book illustration that depicts a pair of wooden chairs with identical fabric covers, see Machida 1988, p. 160, no. 23. For information on Chinese furniture, see Ellsworth 1996; Ellsworth 1997; Wang 1986; Wang 1990.

4   Myers 1989, p. 131.

5   Myers 1989, pp. 131–132.

6   AEDTA inventory number 2228. See Myers 1989, p. 127, fig. 1.

10 Silk Chair Cover with Decoration of Three Dragons against a Patterned Ground

Qing dynasty, late 19th–early 20th century
   Silk brocade; black silk ground of dyed yarns in drawloom or jacquard-loom weave,
   the ground interwoven in brocade weave with gold-wrapped yarns
H. 237.5 cm; W. 60.0 cm (including selvages)

Made as a cover for a chair, this long, rectangular, vertically oriented silk textile not only is much longer than the previous chair cover (number 9) but is divided into just three compositional sections rather than four. Appearing upside down when the textile is displayed as a vertical panel, the dragon roundel at the top would have been suspended over the top of the chair to secure the cover in place and to ornament the chair's rear face. The elongated dragon at the center of the textile would have covered the chair's back splat and then continued over the seat. The roundel at the bottom—a mirror image of the dragon roundel at the top—would have hung from the front edge of the seat, concealing the open area below the chair. Each of the narrow borders of unembellished satin ground that frames the textile top and bottom terminates in a short fringe of exposed warp-yarn ends. Woven with silk yarns wrapped with yellow-gold-embellished paper, an elaborate key fret pattern stretches between the two plain borders; interrupted only by the dragon roundels at top and bottom, the key fret pattern lends visual unity to this textile, while serving as a foil for its elongated central dragon. (By contrast, the dragons in the roundels appear against grounds of plain black satin.) Inspired by the *leiwen*, or squared spiral patterns, that ornament the backgrounds of bronze ritual vessels from the Shang (c. 16th century B.C.–c. 1028 B.C.) and Zhou (c. 1028 B.C.–221 B.C.) dynasties, the key fret pattern not only brings a classical air to this textile but links it to the so-called "later bronzes", made in the Ming and Qing periods, which also evoke the spirit of early bronzes.[1] Depicted frontally and peering out at the viewer, each of this textile's three dragons coils about a flaming jewel. The wisps of flame emanating from their joints echo the dragons' bristling whiskers, horns, and manes; more importantly, they symbolize the dragons' extraordinary powers. The gold-embellished supplementary weft yarns used for the key fret pattern are smaller in diameter than those used for the dragon motifs. In fact, the dragons utilize two different types of gold-embellished yarns: one type appears pink—perhaps due to the application of red gold leaf instead of yellow gold leaf—and was employed for the dragons' faces, horns, scales, and claws; a second type appears yellow and was employed for the dragons' mouths, noses, eyes, manes, spinal ridges, talons, and outlines. The flaming jewels boast a disk of yellow gold surrounded by a circle of pink gold; their wisps of flame, like those emanating from the dragons' joints, are of yellow gold. In all instances, the gold-faced supplementary wefts are bundles of silk fibers about which have been wrapped narrow strips of paper to which gold leaf has been applied over a ground of bole on the obverse. Both selvages are present; because they have been folded under the textile, they are not visible on the obverse. The gold-wrapped supplementary silk wefts used for the brocaded key fret background are continuous across the textile; they float on the reverse where not needed for the design scheme. The key fret pattern extends to within 2.8 cm of each selvage; at the edges, the gold-wrapped wefts used for the pattern reverse direction and continue across the fabric in the opposite direction. The gold-wrapped supplementary wefts used for the dragon motifs are discontinuous, appearing only in the three dragon-emblazoned areas; cut where not needed for the brocade pattern, those metallic weft yarns do not extend across the full width of the textile.

The five-clawed dragons and the extensive use of gold suggest that this chair cover and its mate were made for palace use. The virtually perfect condition further suggests that this cover was never used.

Both the black-and-gold color scheme and the use of two hues of gold date this elegant chair cover to the late nineteenth or early twentieth century. In addition, the division of the textile into three, instead of four, compositional sections supports this late Qing attribution as does the unification of the design scheme through the use of the key fret pattern.

68 [RDM]

Technical Analysis

Warp: Black silk; S twist; single ply. Count: 80 yarns per centimeter. Other: There are complementary sets of warp yarns—that is, a warp yarn visible on the obverse of the fabric is paired with a warp yarn visible on the reverse. *Weft*: Foundation: Black silk; Z twist; three ply, slight S. Count: 24 yarns per centimeter. Supplementary: There are two types of supplementary weft yarns, both of which are silk yarns wrapped with gold leaf on a ground of bole over a paper substrate. 1) Yellow silk; Z twist; single ply; the yarns are tightly wrapped (Z twist wrapping) with gold leaf on a ground of bole over a paper substrate. This yarn is much smaller in diameter than the other supplementary wefts. Location: Type-one supplementary weft yarns are used throughout the ground of the textile to create the gold diaper pattern. 2) One type is green silk yarn, one type is orange silk yarn; slight Z twist; 2 ply. Z twist; the yarns are loosely wrapped (Z twist wrapping) with gold leaf on a ground of bole over a paper substrate. Type-two supplementary weft yarns are used in localized areas of the textile to create the three dragon motifs. The green and orange yarns are prepared in identical manner, so their technical descriptions are identical, except for the colors of their silk cores. Because they are visible through the interstices of the loosely wrapped, gold-embellished paper, the green and orange colors of the silk cores influence the viewer's perception of the finished yarns. *Weave*: Brocade. Woven on a drawloom or on a jacquard loom. There are two types of brocading—that used for the diapered background and that used for the dragon motifs. 1) The brocading used for the diapered background extends to within 2.8 cm of each selvage. The wefts (type-one supplementary wefts) are continuous and float on the reverse where not needed for the brocade pattern; at the edges, they reverse direction and continue across the fabric in the opposite direction. 2) The brocading used for the dragon motifs is discontinuous; that is, it is used only in the three dragon-emblazoned areas. Thus, the supplementary metallic weft yarns used for the dragon motifs do not extend across the full width of the textile; rather, the wefts (type-two supplementary wefts) are cut where not needed for the brocade pattern and thus they do not float on the reverse. Other: Were the warp and weft yarns the same color, the brocading of the diapered background would be termed a satin weave damask. However, they are not the same color in this textile; in addition, a compound weave that incorporates a metallic yarn is traditionally termed a brocade. Hence, for various reasons, the diapered background of this textile is termed a brocade weave, despite its resemblance to a satin weave. Condition: Excellent. The color is vibrant and the weave is in superior condition. The reverse shows numerous long loops of metallic weft yarns; this unusual situation likely resulted from technical difficulties encountered in weaving with metallic yarns. Dyeing: Yarn dyed. *Selvages*: Both selvages are present. (The selvages have been folded under so that they are not visible on the obverse.) Black warp yarns are bundled together to make thick warps for the selvages; in like manner, two black weft yarns are bundled together to make thick wefts for the selvages. Count: 14 warp yarns per centimeter; 12 weft yarn per centimeter. Weave: Tabby weave.

[MWG]

1   For information about later Chinese bronzes, see Phoenix 1983.

69

10

酒自宋人乃宗不兩好

古有意無之之有内

董其昌书

Numbers 11–19   Tapestries

11

[Front]

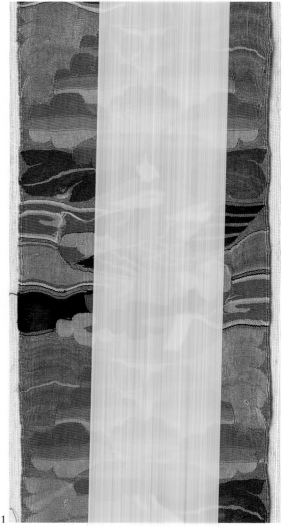

11

[Detail: back]

11 Rectangular Silk Panel with Decoration of Rock, Peonies, and Phoenixes

Ming dynasty, 15th century
   Silk *kesi* tapestry; dyed polychrome silk yarns and gold-wrapped yarns
   in weft-faced tabby-weave fabric utilizing the *kesi* tapestry technique to create
   representational patterns
H. 48.0 cm; W. 12.6 cm, including selvages

This small, rectangular panel of boldly colored silk tapestry depicts two multicolored phoenixes, or *fenghuang*, that hover amidst the red blossoms of a tree peony plant growing beside a blue garden rock. At the bottom of the composition, a stream with white-edged ripples flows past a tall, perforated garden rock, whose lower half is medium blue and whose upper half is navy blue. Emerging from behind the rock on a sinewy stalk of pale gray, the tree peony rises to the top of the composition, its two large blossoms rhythmically placed and stretching the full width of the textile. Each blossom boasts five tiers of overlapping petals arrayed about a yellow heart representing a cluster of pistils and stamens; horizontally striated in graded hues of red (from pink to rose to terracotta), each petal has scalloped edges. A tier of descending petals indicates that a third blossom once appeared at the top of the composition. The segmented tail with three barbed filaments identifies as male the descending phoenix that appears beneath the partial blossom at the top of the panel; by contrast, the scrolling tail identifies as female the ascending phoenix that appears between the two full blossoms. A six-lobed red comb crowns each bird's head. Both phoenixes look toward the textile's proper right, though they fly in opposite directions: the male, upper bird toward the proper left and the female, lower bird toward the right. Large, lobed leaves in various shades of green—from pale green to bluish celadon green to dark hunter green—project laterally from behind the blossoms, each leaf with a central vein in a contrasting color. Brightly hued, scrolling clouds flank the phoenixes; visible along the sides of the textile and immediately above and below each phoenix, small areas woven with gold-wrapped threads represent the sky. Careful examination reveals that the obverse has faded (due to exposure to light), so that its colors are duller than those of the reverse. Both selvages are present, demonstrating that this textile preserves its full, original width; by contrast, the irregular, frayed edges and interrupted design motifs indicate that it has been cut at top and bottom, so that the present composition is incomplete. We cannot know the date this panel was cut from the original textile, just as we cannot know either the length of the original textile or the exact nature of its design scheme (whether repeating or continuously evolving, for example). Employing no supplementary weft yarns, this warp-faced, tabby-weave textile relies solely upon its foundation wefts for both its structure and its decoration. Because the textile is woven in *kesi* tapestry technique, individual weft threads do not extend the full width from selvage to selvage; rather, weft threads of specified color are used in localized areas, each thread reversing direction within the weave at the edge of its area of specified color. The wefts are cut close to the weave and the ends are typically hidden within the weave, so that they are invisible; when visible, the cut ends always appear on the reverse. (Thus, with minor exceptions, the fronts and backs of *kesi* tapestry-weave textiles, including this striking example, are the same.) Because individual weft threads of a defined color change direction within the weave, narrow, vertical openings—traditionally termed slits or slit joins—appear between horizontally adjacent areas of different color (clearly visible between the red petals and the green leaves, for example). For the background areas, which might be read as sky, this textile employs gold-embellished weft threads—a bundled core of pale yellow silk fibers around which is wrapped a narrow strip of paper whose outer face has been embellished with gold leaf over a ground of bole. Most of the gold leaf is still present, so the gold-embellished areas are lustrous and golden.

Its size, shape, and proportions suggest that this textile might once have served as the cover for a Buddhist sutra, or holy text;[1] as such, it would have been mounted on heavy cardboard and then affixed to the front or back of an accordion-fold sutra, which is typically tall, slender, and vertically oriented.[2] A paper title slip likely would have been glued to the front face of such a sutra; measuring approximately thirty centimeters in height and four centimeters in width, the title slip would have been centered on the sutra's vertical axis, its top aligned with that of the sutra. Even if this panel once served as the cover of a sutra, however, the original textile from which it was cut surely was not made for that purpose. Longer than the present panel, the original textile perhaps was woven as a long, narrow strip; although we can only guess at its function, such a long, vertically oriented strip of fabric with stylized pictorial decor might have been designed as a border, perhaps for a robe[3] or for a decorative panel (see discussion below).

History records that the indigenous tree peony (*Paeonia arborea*) was introduced into the imperial gardens in the late sixth or early seventh century, during the short-lived Sui dynasty (581–618).[4] With its large, showy blossoms, the tree peony quickly captured the imagination of the Chinese, who began to cultivate it on a wide scale; it numbered among the most popular flowers in the realm by the eighth century and has retained its appeal to the present day. The peony frequently appears in Tang-dynasty Buddhist paintings and in the ornament of Tang gold and silver vessels; numerous secular paintings of blossoming peonies survive from the Song dynasty, typically painted in colors on silk. The peony and the lotus rank among the most popular motifs on Song-dynasty ceramics, particularly in the carved and molded designs on celadon-glazed vessels from the Yaozhou kilns. (In fact, the peonies represented in this *kesi* panel descend from those represented on Yaozhou wares.[5]) The lotus and the peony also figure prominently in the decorative schemes both of Yuan and early Ming blue-and-white porcelains from Jingdezhen and of early Ming carved red lacquer.

Often called the King of Flowers, or *huawang*, due both to its popularity and to the size of its flowers, the tree peony is formally known in Chinese as *mudan hua*, which means "male vermilion flower" and indicates that it is looked upon as the flower associated with the *yang*, or male, principle in the dualistic *yin-yang* system of cosmology. It is, however, also regarded as a symbol of feminine beauty and as an emblem of love and affection. Representing spring, the tree peony figures among the flowers of the four seasons, standing alongside the lotus, chrysanthemum, and plum which, respectively, stand for summer, autumn, and winter; in addition, the peony represents the third month in the Chinese lunar calendar, which generally corresponds to late March and much of April in the Western, Gregorian calendar. Because of its abundant petals, the tree peony is viewed as a symbol of wealth and honor, often termed *fugui hua* (literally, honor [and] wealth flower), so its appearance is regarded as an auspicious wish to the viewer.

As noted above (number 1), traditional Chinese believed the phoenix to be an auspicious bird that appeared in times of peace and prosperity and that symbolized the sun and warmth, and, by association, the south. Through the Han dynasty, the phoenix was customarily depicted as one of the four divine creatures (*siling*) or as one of the four directional symbols. Beginning in the Six Dynasties period, when it came to be shown independently, and continuing through the Tang, the phoenix was typically portrayed striding, with legs extended and wings outstretched.[6] By the Northern Song, the bird was characteristically shown in flight, and by the Southern Song, it was usually paired either with another phoenix or with a *luan*, a mythical bird for which there is no English name. The differing tails clearly distinguish the two birds in this textile. With its long, trailing, segmented tail, the upper bird answers to traditional descriptions of the phoenix; though otherwise identical, the lower bird has a scrolling tail, which might identify it either as a *huang* (female phoenix) or a *luan*.

Meaning "phoenix", the Chinese term *fenghuang* comprises two syllables, with *feng* referring to the male and *huang* to the female. By the late fourteenth century, when the phoenix had come to symbolize both the empress and the *yin*, or female, forces of the universe, male and female phoenixes were not only shown in pairs, but were clearly differentiated by their tails: the male's boasted five major segments while the female's included only two. In other contexts, as in this Clague textile, the male might be shown with a tail of just three barbed segments, in which case the female is portrayed with a scrolling tail.

Chinese artisans apparently began to weave *kesi* tapestries during the Northern Song period, perhaps inspired by *kesi*-type tapestries produced in Eastern Central Asia.[7] The bold, stylized flowers with horizontal bands of bold color suggest that this tapestry dates to the fifteenth century, that is, from the first half of the Ming dynasty. Seemingly absent in Song and Yuan depictions of phoenixes, the lobed combs atop the birds' heads also point to an early Ming date for this textile, as does the division of the female phoenix's tail into a series of five foliate scrolls in contrast to the single, elaborate scroll characteristic of earlier representations.[8]

Depicting numerous birds of varied type, a large *kesi* panel in the collection of the Association pour l'Étude et la Documentation des Textiles d'Asie, Paris, claims as its proper left border a single, narrow *kesi* panel whose pictorial composition is closely related to the present Clague collection textile.[9] Although the AEDTA panel lacks the Clague collection tapestry's phoenix birds, the two pieces are otherwise similar in representing a tree peony with large red blossoms and laterally projecting leaves in various shades of green, all growing on a sinewy stalk that emerges from behind a wave-washed blue rock. Similar in style, the panels must have been produced at roughly the same time—probably in the fifteenth century—though small differences in style indicate that they did not come from the same original fabric. Despite their horizontal orientations and their different subject matter—standing or walking figures separated by large red peony blossoms—two pairs of early Ming *kesi* sutra covers in the collection of the Association pour l'Étude et la Documentation des Textiles d'Asie, Paris, are also closely related in style.[10] Like those in the Clague panel, the lobed peony blossoms in the AEDTA sutra covers are horizontally striated in graded hues of red (from pink to rose to terracotta); in addition, the striking juxtapositions of bold colors arranged in broad horizontal bands link all these works, suggesting that they were done about the same time, perhaps by the same workshop.

[RDM]

Publications: Francesca Galloway and Jacqueline Simcox, *The Art of Textiles*,
             dealer's cat., Spink and Son, London, 1989, p. 28, no. 26.

Technical analysis

Warp: Gray silk; Z twist; 2 ply Z. Count: 15 to 18 per centimeter. The warp yarns extend beyond the weaving at the top and bottom of the textile; the top and bottom edges are not finished. *Weft*: There are weft yarns of many different colors but all are part of the foundation weave; although there are two types of foundation-weft yarns, there are no supplementary weft yarns. Foundation: 1) Polychrome silk; slight S twist; 3-ply, S. Count: 24 yarns per centimeter. 2) Bundles of yellow silk yarns wrapped with gold leaf on a ground of bole over a paper substrate; gold wrap is Z twist; no ply, simply bundles of yellow silk yarns. Count: 24 yarns per centimeter. The gold-wrapped weft yarns in the body of the textile are in good condition. The gold-wrapped weft yarns along the side selvages have lost surface and have subsequently lost shine. In some instances, the cores of bundled yellow silk yarns are exposed because the gold wrapping has been lost. *Weave*: *Kesi* tapestry. The textile is woven in the tapestry technique (weft-faced tabby weave) with slit joins. There is eccentric weaving in the curves. If the distance between two areas where a weft yarn of a particular color is needed is short, the weft yarn passes on the reverse from one area to the next; by contrast, if the distance between areas is long, the weft yarn is cut; thus, the ends of some weft threads are exposed on the reverse. Condition: Faded due to photo-chemical damage. Weft yarns are missing in eight areas, exposing the warp yarns. There are soiled weft yarns in a localized area near the bottom of the textile. *Dyeing*: Yarn dyed. *Selvages*: Both selvages are present; appearing on either side, they run the entire length of the textile. The selvages are woven in weft-faced weave; each is 0.3 cm in width (i.e., two warps wide). Other: The selvage is recognized because the two outermost warps on each side differ from the other warps. The outside warps have six yarns in them; the next warps each include four yarns. All wefts turn around the outermost warp on the two selvages.

[MWG]

1   It should be noted that although they typically measure between 12.5 and 13.0 cm in width, vertically oriented, silk covers for accordion-fold sutras seldom exceed 40.0 cm in height. Measuring 48.0 cm in height, this textile is taller than most such sutra covers; whether or not its greater height and more elongated proportions have any bearing on its possible use as a sutra cover remains unknown. It also has been suggested that this panel might have functioned as the silk wrapper for a sutra mounted in handscroll format (or even for a painted handscroll); though impossible to rule out, that function seems unlikely in this case, as most surviving handscroll wrappers are square or, if rectangular, approximate proportions of two-to-one rather than this example's very elongated proportions of four-to-one. See New York 1997, pp. 82–84, nos. 20–21.

2   For information on Chinese sutra covers, see Polonyi 1970.

3   This suggestion was made verbally to Robert D. Mowry by Jacqueline Simcox on 22 March 2000.

4   For information on the tree peony, see Keswick 1986, pp. 181–183.

5   Compare Gray 1984, color pl. B (opposite p. 49).

6   See Cambridge 1996, p. 83, no. 2.

7   For information on the history and development of silk *kesi* tapestries in China, including discussions of the meaning of the term *kesi*, see "Kesi: Silk Tapestry," chapter 2 in New York 1997, pp. 53–105; Cammann 1948; New York 1971; National Palace Museum 1970; Yang et al. 1983; "Antiquarianism and Naturalism," chapter 10 in New York 1976, pp. 219–255 (particularly pp. 249–255).

8   Contrast the Yuan-dynasty representations of phoenixes in New York 1997, p. 196, fig. 82, p. 197, no. 60; Cambridge 1996, p. 254, no. 103.

9   AEDTA inventory number 1744. See Myers 1989, p. 135, fig. 6.

10 AEDTA inventory numbers 2418, 2419, 2072, 2212. See Riboud et al. 1996, n.p., pls. 20, 21; for AEDTA no. 2149 (only), see Myers 1989, pp. 138–139, fig. 9.

12 Ogival Throne Cover with Decoration of a Dragon Coiled about a Flaming Pearl amidst Scrolling Clouds

Ming dynasty, first half 17th century
  Silk *kesi* tapestry; dyed polychrome silk yarns, gold-wrapped yarns, and
  peacock-feather-filament-embellished yarns in weft-faced tabby-weave fabric
  utilizing the *kesi* tapestry technique to create representational patterns
H. 84.0 cm; W. (max.) 94.0 cm

In the form of an ogival arch, this throne cover was fashioned by stitching together seven pieces cut from a Chinese *kesi* silk tapestry (see diagram). The two sides, each with three rounded lobes, rise from the flat base to terminate in a lotus-petal point at the top. Looking directly out at the viewer, a four-clawed dragon dramatically coiled around a flaming pearl and surrounded by scrolling clouds of varied hue dominates the decorative scheme. The dragon is green in color and thus symbolizes the east, with which it is traditionally associated. Horned, whiskered, and maned, the dragon rises above the rolling, variegated waves at the bottom, its lower paws firmly planted on the triangular peaks of blue and green that jut from the white-capped waters. Employing no supplementary weft yarns, this warp-faced, tabby-weave textile relies solely upon its foundation wefts for both structure and decoration. Because the textile is woven in *kesi* tapestry technique, individual weft threads do not extend the full width of the textile (or even of the pieces into which the original textile was cut); rather, weft threads of specified color are used in localized areas, each thread reversing direction within the weave at the edge of its area of specified color. The wefts are cut close to the weave and the ends are typically hidden within the weave, so that they are usually invisible. (Thus, with minor exception, the fronts and backs of *kesi* tapestry-weave textiles, including this example, are the same.) Because individual weft threads of a defined color change direction within the weave, narrow, vertical slit joins that run parallel to the warp threads appear between horizontally adjacent areas of different color. The background areas, which might be read as the sky in which the dragon and clouds appear, employ gold-embellished weft threads—a bundled core of white silk fibers around which is wrapped a narrow strip of paper whose outer face has been embellished with gold leaf over a ground of bole. In addition, gold-embellished threads outline the features of the dragon's face, just as they accentuate the scales of its body. Such gold-embellished weft threads also outline the blue-and-green mountains that project through the rolling waves at the bottom of the composition, just as gold pigment is often used to outline the rocks and mountains in traditional blue-and-green-style paintings on paper or silk.[1] Most of the gold leaf is still present, so the gold-embellished areas are lustrous and golden. The use of weft threads embellished with peacock-feather filaments distinguishes this textile from other luxury silks in the Clague collection. Used for the deep, mottled, hunter green areas of the textile—the dragon's paws, portions of its face, the darkest of its scales, the outlines describing its white horns, and the darkest portion of the flaming pearl—the feather-embellished threads were prepared by interweaving peacock-feather filaments with medium green silk yarn. Because the feather filaments are interwoven with the silk yarn, rather than tightly wrapped around it, both the iridescent filaments and the medium green yarn are visible, a circumstance that imparts vibrant, mottled color and rich,

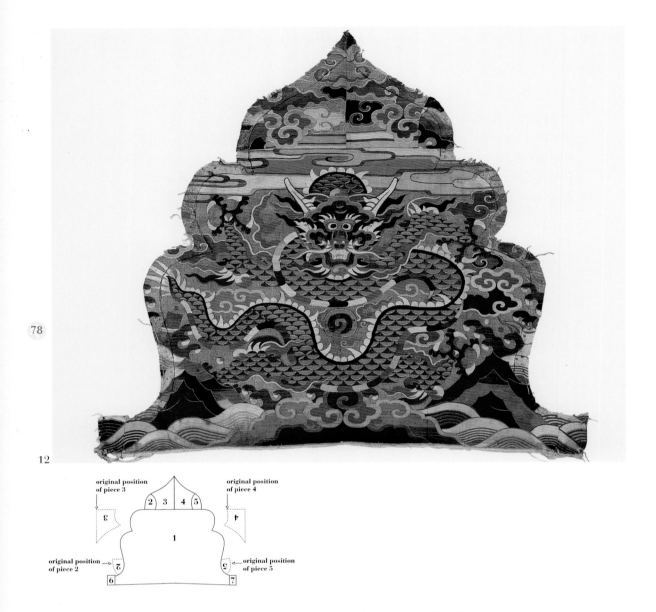

12

varied texture. The peacock-feather filaments have been scientifically identified as having come from the tail of an Indian Peafowl (*Pavo cristatus*).[2] Since an original textile was cut into pieces and reassembled to fashion this throne cover, no edges claim long, continuous stretches of selvage; however, edges of four pieces incorporated into this cover terminate in short sections of selvages. Each of the two pieces at the top center—sewn together to form the lotus-petal point—has a length of selvage at its inside edge (pieces 3 and 4); visible on the reverse, the selvages appear at the vertical seam that joins the two pieces. In addition, areas of selvage appear on the outside edges of the two small pieces (pieces 6 and 7) stitched to the bottom of the main, or central, panel at right and left. The colors on the obverse are slightly brighter than those of the reverse, which have faded slightly due to exposure to light.

The seven pieces stitched together to form the present throne cover all came from the same original textile; in fact, this cover preserves much of that original *kesi* panel, if in rearranged configuration. Pieces 3 and 4—that is, the generally triangular pieces that are now joined to form the lotus-petal point—originally appeared just outside the middle lobes of the present throne cover and thus extended laterally the band of scrolling clouds that flanks the dragon's head. Piece 3 appeared adjacent to the proper right lobe and piece 4 adjacent to the proper left lobe; the two pieces are completely reversed from their original orientation—that is, each piece would have appeared upside down in relation to its present orientation and would have been

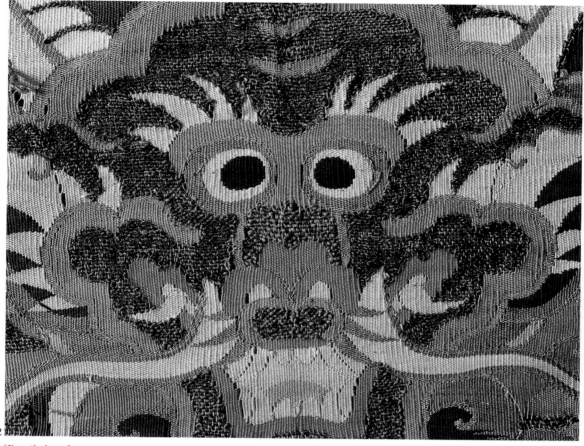

12

[Detail: front]

12

[Detail: back]

"flipped" in terms of right/left orientation—so that the two selvages that are concealed within the vertical seam at top center would have been sections of the original textile's selvages, at its outer edges. This circumstance suggests that the present throne cover preserves much of the original textile's width. Pieces 2 and 5, which flank the lotus-petal point, were originally situated toward the bottom of the textile, adjacent to the areas with the blue-and-green mountains, their colors and forms continuing those of the wave-washed mountains; careful examination reveals the exact locations from which they were cut. Pieces 6 and 7—the very small pieces at the outside edges along the bottom—appear to be generally in their original positions, though moved inward a bit; a small section of fabric probably was removed from each side in those areas in order to decrease the width of the throne cover (rather than per se to reposition pieces 6 and 7).[3] In this reconstruction of the original *kesi* panel, the small sections of selvage present at the outside edges of pieces 6 and 7 would be almost directly below the sections of selvage on pieces 3 and 4, suggesting that the bottom of the present throne cover preserves most of the width of the original textile. The salmon colored edging along the lowermost edge indicates that the bottom of the throne cover was also the bottom of the original textile. The exact height of the original kesi panel cannot be determined with certainty; however, since only a few more clouds would have appeared above the head of the dragon, the throne cover's central piece (piece 1) probably preserves most of the original *kesi* panel's height. If these suppositions are correct, we may be justified in concluding that the original textile was a rectangular panel whose width was approximately one and one-half times its height. That the colors are brighter on the present front face than on the back suggests that the original textile was turned inside out when it was cut into pieces and reassembled as a throne cover, so that the original reverse now serves as the throne cover's obverse, a circumstance made possible because the front and back faces of high-quality *kesi* tapestries are virtually identical. The ogival-arch shape suggests that the original *kesi* panel was cut into pieces and fashioned into a throne cover in Tibet; although the date the throne cover was fashioned cannot be known, the fading of the colors on the reverse strongly suggests that the textile served another function before it was transformed into a throne cover.

The appearance of the dragon-and-pearl motif and the use of both peacock-feather filaments and gold-embellished threads suggests that the original *kesi* panel was made for a robe. In that context, the original panel doubtless served as the robe's back, as Ming robes typically featured a single dragon coiled about a flaming pearl on the back and two facing, vertically oriented dragons on the front, each reaching for one of the two flaming pearls at the robe's collar.[4] The absence of a long, diagonal cut across the throne cover's main section (piece 1) further indicates that the original textile did not serve as the front panel of a robe; had it been incorporated into a robe's front, a diagonal cut would have been necessary to permit the robe to be opened. Such a robe would have had stitched to its bottom as a broad border another *kesi* panel representing rolling, white-capped waves, thus amplifying the theme of churning waters that appears at the bottom of this throne cover.

Woven during the first half of the seventeenth century, this textile reflects the Ming taste for bold patterns set against brightly colored, horizontally striated grounds, the striated grounds typically interpreted as bands of scrolling clouds. The present textile and its congeners represent an evolution and development of the early Ming style, as represented by the Clague collection's small vertical *kesi* panel with peony and rock décor (number 11). The bright colors that describe the scales on this dragon's belly recall the bright colors that are typically juxtaposed on textiles and ceramics made during the Jiajing reign (1522–1566) (see discussion number 5);

however, the colors in this seventeenth-century textile are both more numerous (including olive brown and khaki as well as lavender and pink) and more complex (including multiple shades of blue, for example) than those that occur in sixteenth-century works. In addition, peacock-feather filaments were first incorporated into Chinese silk textiles in the late sixteenth or early seventeenth century, a feature that further attests to this fabric's late Ming date. The inclusion of such iridescent filaments reflects the continuing Ming effort to extend the palette to its most varied and diverse possibilities. The style of the dragon also dates this textile to the first half of the seventeenth century; in particular, the five-lobed cranium, the barbed white eyebrows with four spikes each, the short horns each with three thickened rings at its base, the white dorsal ridge with a repeating series of four rounded lobes set between barbed lobes, the polychrome belly scales, and the semicircular body scales horizontally arrayed are all characteristics peculiar to the first half of the seventeenth century. The results of a radiocarbon test conducted by Timothy Jull at The University of Arizona NSF-Arizona AMS Facility, Tucson, on a small sample removed from this textile are consistent with the seventeenth-century date proposed here.[5]

Incorporating both gold-embellished threads and peacock-feather filament into its decorative scheme, a *kesi* dragon robe now in the care of Jobrenco Limited, trustee, Hall Collection Trust, is identical to the Clague collection throne cover in weaving materials and techniques. Since the two are closely related in style, both have been assigned to the first half of the seventeenth century.[6] Now in the collection of the Ferenc Hopp Museum of Eastern Asiatic Arts, Budapest, a sutra cover fashioned from a fragment of a late Ming dragon robe of brocaded silk is distantly related to the Clague collection throne cover in style;[7] its sixteenth-to-seventeenth-century attribution bolsters the attribution of the Clague throne cover to the seventeenth century.

[RDM]

Publications: Claudia Brown, "The Amy S. Clague Collection of Chinese Textiles," *Orientations* 31, no. 2 (February 2000), pp. 36–37, figs. 7, 7a.

Technical analysis

Warp: Off-white silk; S twist; 2 ply, Z. Count: 16 yarns per centimeter. *Weft*: There are three different types of weft yarns and all are part of the foundation tapestry weave. There are no supplementary wefts. 1) Polychrome silk; S twist; 2 ply, Z. Count: 18 to 25 yarns per centimeter. Condition: Some colors have faded. In particular, the light peach-colored weft yarns have faded; they originally were a darker, brighter peach color. In addition, some of the medium blue yarns include streaks of white. Those areas of white are not damage; rather, they are areas of the yarn that did not accept dye. Other: Eccentric weaving occurs in those areas of the design with curving outlines, creating a variance in the yarn count. In those areas where a weft thread of a particular color is needed for the design scheme just a short distance from where previously used, that weft thread is not cut; rather, it floats either over or under warp threads to the location where it is next needed. Such floats do not exceed 1.5 cm in length. 2) Bundles of white silk yarns wrapped with gold leaf on a ground of pink bole over a white paper substrate; gold wrap is Z twist. Count: 16 yarns per centimeter. Condition: Although some of the gold-embellished yarns are abraded, most are in good condition so that they impart a lustrous, metallic effect. 3) Peacock-feather filaments and bundled silk fibers twisted together; green silk, brown with sparkle of pink and green; Z twist; single ply. Count: 11 yarns per centimeter. Condition: Excellent; very little damage of any kind. Other: These weft yarns were examined by Beth Ann Sabo (of Wildlife Forensic Services, Irving, Texas), who found the iridescent pink and green sparkles—technically, barbules rather than sparkles—to be diagnostic of Indian peafowl feathers. Microscopic comparison of feather fibers from the textile and actual peafowl feathers confirms that the barbs in the textile are consistent with barbs of the feathers of male peafowl. The materials bundled with the silk fibers and interwoven into the textile are the long, widely spaced, and highly iridescent barbs subtending the "eye" feathers of the peafowl. Such barbs exhibit a brown rachilla, and iridescent pink/lime green barbules. *Weave*: *Kesi* tapestry. The textile is woven in the tapestry technique (weft-faced tabby weave) with slit joins. In the areas of the peacock-feather-embellished yarns, the weave is a plain tabby weave. Other: The textile is virtually identical on obverse and reverse. Few weft yarn ends show. The weaving of the textile is eccentric in those areas of the design with curving outlines. Condition: The structure of the textile is in good condition. Adhesive residues soil this textile. A line has been drawn in ink around the textile's sides, the line approximately 3.0 centimeters from the edge.

Weft yarns are missing along the proper left side, approximately at the midpoint. There is a small hole in the same area; a small piece of gray fabric has been glued to the textile's reverse to conceal the hole. *Dyeing*: Yarn dyed. *Selvages*: As this throne cover has been pieced together from pieces of fabric cut from a larger textile, sections of the selvage are present only in localized areas. In fact, areas of selvage appear on the outside edges of the two small pieces (pieces 6 and 7) stitched to the bottom of the main, or central, panel (piece 1) at right and left. Each of the two pieces at the top center—sewn together to form the throne cover's lotus-petal point—has a length of selvage at its inside edge (pieces 3 and 4); visible on the reverse, the two selvages appear at the vertical seam that joins the two pieces. The selvages have a weft-faced tabby weave (tapestry). The width of the selvage cannot be determined, as the warp and weft yarns are identical to those in the main fabric. Other: All weft yarns turn around the outermost warp threads on the selvages.

Commentary

This textile comprises seven pieces of fabric hand-sewn together using running stitches and back stitches.

[MWG]

1   For use of blue-and-green landscape conventions in a Chinese *kesi* silk tapestry from the Yuan dynasty, see New York 1997, pp. 101–103, no. 26. For examples of Chinese landscape paintings in the blue-and-green manner, see Fong 1992, pp. 315–319, pls. 70–71.

2   Identified by Beth Ann Sabo, Wildlife Forensic Services, Irving, Texas. The 30 June 1998 Examination Report prepared by Ms. Sabo states:

Examination with a handlens (10x) and dissecting microscope (30–40x) revealed the presence of feather material. The material appeared to be represented by single barbs, rachillas (rami) brown, with filamentous barbules of pennaceous type. The distal barbules are iridescent pink and light (lime) green; barbules are less iridescent on the proximal vanule. At 40x the barbules are decidedly crinkled, much like accordion-folded paper. This characteristic probably increases the reflective feature of the barbules. Crimping at the base of each barb is not natural and probably indicates where it was grasped by mechanical means for weaving purposes.

Showy feathers of this nature are typical of species that commonly exhibit a display behavior, which is generally the male of avian species. The pink/green combination is unusual, and is typical of peafowl. Comparison was made to feathers of Indian Peafowl (*Pavo cristatus*), male.

Microscopic comparison of the textile and peafowl feathers confirms the consistency of the barbs in the textile with barbs of the feathers of male peafowl (=peacock). Specifically, the interwoven materials are the long, widely-spaced, and highly iridescent barbs subtending the "eye" feathers of the peacock. These barbs exhibit a brown rachilla, and iridescent pink/lime green barbules. The crinkled appearance of the pennaceous barbules and other morphologies compare favorably.

Note: The barbs exhibiting the pink/lime green combination are found exclusively in the textile; no iridescent blue barbs were found.

In addition, feathers or feather parts from other species were not determined to be present.

There are two species of peafowl, the Indian peafowl (*Pavo cristatus*) and the Javan or Green Peafowl (*Pavo muticus*). The availability of Indian Peafowl and the match in morphological features of this species to the unknown material in the textile indicate Indian Peafowl as the species represented.

3   It is unclear why pieces 6 and 7 were removed and then reattached. It is possible that a section was cut from each side to decrease the width of the bottom; if too much fabric was removed, perhaps pieces 6 and 7 were reattached to restore the bottom to the required width. Alternatively, perhaps pieces 6 and 7 were reattached because each preserves a section of selvage at its outside edge, which would help to prevent the bottom's sides from unraveling; this seems a most unlikely scenario, however, since no other sections of selvage were incorporated into any other of this throne cover's outside edges.

4   See Hong Kong 1995, pp. 202–203, no. 55; 206–207, no. 57.

5   Sample date number: AA-31552. According to Timothy Jull, on the basis of the radiocarbon tests, this textile can be assigned to the period 1663–1946 with sixty eight per cent confidence or to the period 1657–1947 with ninety five per cent confidence. Letter dated 23 February 1999 from A.J.T. Jull, The University of Arizona NSF-Arizona AMS Facility, Tucson, to Claudia Brown, Research Curator for Asian Art, Phoenix Art Museum. The actual date of a piece is just as likely to be at either end of a range of dates deduced from the interpretation of radiocarbon tests as it is to be at the midpoint of the range. This textile likely was woven in the closing years of the Ming dynasty, just before it collapsed in 1644.

6   See Hong Kong 1995, pp. 206–207, no. 57.

7   Ferenc Hopp Museum inventory number 51.476. See Polonyi 1970, pp. 92, no. 2; 99, fig. 1, no. 2.

13 Rectangular Sutra Cover with the Eight Auspicious Emblems (*Bajixiang*) Set within a Border of Ten Striding Dragons Pursuing Flaming Jewels

Qing dynasty, probably Qianlong reign (1736–1795)
Silk *kesi* tapestry; dyed polychrome silk yarns and gold-wrapped yarns in weft-faced tabby-weave fabric utilizing the *kesi* tapestry technique to create representational patterns
H. 14.5 cm; W. (max.) 52.5–53.5 cm

13

Designed as a sutra cover and woven in *kesi* tapestry technique, this horizontally oriented, rectangular panel of silk features as its principal decorative motif the Eight Auspicious Emblems, or *bajixiang*, set within a border of five-clawed dragons, each in pursuit of a flaming jewel. Reading from left to right, the auspicious emblems appear in the following order:

Umbrella (*san* or *gai*) symbolizing royal grace
Double Fish (*yu*) symbolizing fertility, abundance, conjugal
    happiness, and protection against evil
Vase or Jar (*ping*) symbolizing eternal harmony, abundant
    blessings, and ultimate triumph over birth and death
Flower (*hua*) symbolizing truth, purity, and creative power
Conch Shell (*luo*) symbolizing majesty, felicitous travel, and the
    voice of the Buddha
Endless Knot (*jie*) symbolizing longevity, eternity, and receipt
    of the Buddha's assistance
Canopy (*chuang*) symbolizing spiritual authority, reverence,
    and purity
Wheel (*lun*) symbolizing the Wheel of the Law (*falun*) and thus
    the Buddha and His teachings[1]

Featured against a sky-blue background, each emblem rests on a five-petaled lotus blossom. Each lotus support has five descending pink petals, edged in azure, arrayed about a stepped, four-lobed, celadon-green center whose flat top boasts a series of small circles suggestive of seed pods. Decorative ribbons of varied hue flutter on either side of each emblem, save the flower, where stylized leaves appropriately replace the ribbons. A red ornament, in some instances a flaming jewel, crowns many of the emblems. A formal vegetal scroll with stylized leaves of green and blue links the lotus supports, one to the next; a tendril branches from the scroll to encircle each emblem and its associated lotus-blossom support. Two pairs of golden bowstring lines frame this cover's wide, dragon borders; the outer pair delineates the cover's edges while the inner pair distinguishes the border from the principal register of decoration. Similarly embellished, the top and bottom borders each boast four striding dragons, all facing inward and all shown in profile. The two inner dragons reach for the single flaming jewel at the border's center; each outer dragon reaches for the flaming jewel that floats on a cloud just to the rear of the inner dragon that it follows. The single dragon in each vertical side border strides upward, grasping for the flaming jewel that appears in the corner above; the tails of the vertical dragons' tails fill the lower corners. In this arrangement, five flaming jewels punctuate the upper border but only three appear in the lower border. Though very similar, the top and bottom borders vary slightly because of the differing treatment of the corners; by contrast, the two side borders are bilaterally symmetrical. Employing no supplementary weft yarns, this warp-faced, tabby-weave textile relies solely upon its foundation wefts for both structure and decoration. Because the textile is woven in *kesi* tapestry technique, individual weft threads do not extend the full width of the textile, except for some of the threads comprising the sky-blue ground; rather, weft threads of specified color are used in localized areas, each thread reversing direction within the weave at the edge of its area of specified color. The wefts are cut close to the weave and the ends are typically hidden within the weave, so that they are usually invisible. (Although a sheet of paper glued to the back prevents detailed examination of this textile's reverse, it is assumed that, following convention, front and back are virtually the same.) Because individual weft threads of a defined color change direction within the weave, narrow, vertical slit joins that run parallel to the warp threads appear between horizontally adjacent areas of different color. The eight emblems, their lotus supports, and the leafy scrolls encircling them were woven with weft threads of colored silk, as were the borders' flaming jewels and the clouds on which they rest; by contrast, the ten dragons and the two pairs of bowstring lines framing them employ gold-embellished weft threads—a bundled core of silk fibers around which is wrapped a narrow strip of paper whose outer face has been embellished with gold leaf over a ground of bole. The bowstring lines comprise solely such metallic threads; although they rely upon gold-wrapped threads for their scales, the dragons also incorporate silk threads of white (for outlines and horns), red (for tongues of flame issuing from joints), and blues and greens (for manes and tufts of fur); in addition, threads of dark blue—and, on alternating dragons, of dark green—interspersed with the gold-wrapped threads impart rich, varied color and texture to the scaled areas of the dragons' bodies. Most of the gold leaf is still present, so the gold-embellished areas are lustrous and golden. Virtually all of the decoration is woven, including the single lines used for outlines and for veins within petals and leaves; however, small areas of subtle shading in the fluttering ribbons, in the green centers of the lotus supports, and in the leaves of the vegetal scrolls may have been delicately touched in with a brush dipped in vegetable pigment. A section of selvage appears along one side; it is probable that another section of selvage, perhaps lost in trimming and mounting, once appeared along the other side; if so, then this sutra cover preserves most of the width of the original textile.

The size, proportions, and horizontal orientation indicate that this textile was intended to cover the title page of the stacked folios of a lavish Tibetan Buddhist manuscript. Julia Meech notes that "often three or four layers of Chinese silks covered a title page, affixed along the top edge with a strip of paper and glue... A wood outer cover, probably encrusted with precious stones, would have completed the ensemble."[2] She further observes that during the Qing, another non-Chinese dynasty, "Tibetan Buddhism and lamas continued to exert considerable influence both at court and important Chinese monasteries. Tibetan books were copied in many of the Chinese monasteries, and the lamas preferred to use Chinese silks to cover both their thankas and their sutras. Chinese factories produced brocade sutra covers and silk curtains for the use of local temples such as the Yonghegong (Yung-ho-kung) in Beijing and also for export to Tibet."³

Introduced to Chinese art from Tibetan Buddhism in the Yuan dynasty, the Eight Auspicious Emblems gained a measure of popularity in the decorative arts of the Ming and Qing dynasties. On this cover for a Tibetan sutra, the motif surely was used more for its symbolism than for its decorative appeal. Made in China, such silk sutra covers typically pair the assimilated Tibetan motif with the traditional Chinese motif of dragons pursuing flaming jewels. The extraordinary

13

[Detail]

13

[Detail]

quality of both design and weaving, together with the ten, five-clawed dragons worked in gold-embellished threads, suggests that this *kesi* tapestry cover was made by imperial command, perhaps for the palace, for an imperial temple, or for presentation to a temple in Tibet.

Sutra covers of lacquered wood had been embellished with gilded images of the Eight Auspicious Emblems at least as early as the Yongle reign (1403–1424) of the Ming dynasty. Set on lotus bases within encircling vegetal scrolls, such Yongle representations are the clear ancestors of this sutra cover's design.[4] (Also compare the scrolling lotus design in the Clague collection's panel of needleloop embroidery, number 21.) However, the shapes of its leaves and the twists of its stems indicate that the scroll on this sutra cover like those on Qing-dynasty sutra covers of related style—takes its inspiration from the very similar scrolls on small porcelain jars with enameled decoration in *doucai* style made at Jingdezhen, Jiangxi province, during the Chenghua reign (1465–1467) of the Ming dynasty.[5]

The auspicious emblems on this sutra cover and its congeners appear in an order very different from that established in the Ming (see discussion, number 5, where the emblems are listed in standard Ming order); in fact, they are arranged according to Qing convention, which gives a clue to the dating of this exquisite piece. The depictions of the eight emblems support the attribution of this sutra cover to the Qianlong reign (1736–1795) of the Qing dynasty,[6] as do the style and configuration of the dragons. In addition, the meticulous craftsmanship—in which every representational element is woven exclusively in *kesi* tapestry weave, with little, if any, painting of details—further points to a mid-eighteenth-century date of manufacture.[7]

Ascribed to the eighteenth century, a sutra cover in the collection of the Association pour l'Étude et la Documentation des Textiles d'Asie, Paris,[8] is identical to the Clague cover except for minor differences in the color of the ribbons that flutter about the auspicious emblems; in fact, the Clague and AEDTA covers are so similar that they originally might have been part of the same set. A set of five silk *kesi* tapestry sutra covers in the Eugene Fuller Memorial Collection at the Seattle Art Museum includes three covers with exactly the same design as the Clague cover; among those three covers, one has a medium green ground, one has a midnight blue ground, and one has an ivory or pale blue ground, similar to that of the Clague cover. Though clearly related, the Seattle covers are not from the same group as the Clague and AEDTA pieces; in fact, their style suggests that they date to the nineteenth century; as such, they probably are descendants of the Clague and AEDTA pieces.[9] Made in China and attributed to the eighteenth century, a related sutra cover in the collection of the State Central Library of Mongolia is similarly ornamented but its decoration is embroidered in satin-stitch embroidery rather than woven in *kesi* tapestry weave.[10]

[RDM]

Publications: Francesca Galloway and Jacqueline Simcox, *The Art of Textiles*, dealer's cat., Spink and Son, London, 1989, p. 29, no. 27, and p. 162, no. 27; Urban Council, Hong Kong, and the Oriental Ceramic Society of Hong Kong in association with the Liaoning Provincial Museum, *Jinxiu luoyi qiao tiangong / Heavens' Embroidered Cloths: One-Thousand Years of Chinese Textiles*, exh. cat., Hong Kong Museum of Art, Hong Kong, 1995, pp. 188–189, no. 49; Rose Lee, "Chinese Textiles Related to Tibetan Buddhism in the Hong Kong Museum of Art," *Arts of Asia* 25, no. 4 (July–August 1995), p. 76, fig. 10; Claudia Brown, "The Amy S. Clague Collection of Chinese Textiles," *Orientations* 31, no. 2 (February 2000), pp. 35–37, figs. 6, 6a.

Technical analysis

Warp: Tan silk; Z twist; 2 ply S. Count: 36 yarns per centimeter. Other: Thin and tightly twisted. *Weft*: There are only two types of weft yarns, though those two types include many different colors. All weft yarns are part of the foundation weave; there are no supplementary wefts. 1) Polychrome silk; Z twist; 2 ply, S. Count: 28 per centimeter. Other: The weft yarns are much bulkier than the warp yarns. 2) Bundled golden yellow silk yarns wrapped with gold leaf on a ground of pink bole over a tan paper substrate; gold wrap is Z twist; no ply—merely a bundle of golden yellow silk yarns. Count: 28 yarns per centimeter. Other: The gold leaf is very thin. Condition: The gold has retained a bright luster. Some of the gold-wrapped threads have unraveled along the borders. *Weave*: *Kesi* tapestry. The textile is woven in the tapestry technique (weft-faced tabby weave) with slit joins. The weaving of the textile is eccentric in those areas of the design with curving outlines; in general, however, the warp and weft yarns are at right angles to one another. The most interesting areas of the weave occur in the vertical borders at the sides; the weaving of the dragons—one vertically placed at either side—required the inclusion of numerous slit joins, which weaken the fabric, making those border areas exceptionally fragile. The many slit joins resulted because weft yarns of a particular color do not pass on the reverse from one area of usage to the next area where needed for the design; rather, the yarns are cut. Other: A layer of paper glued to the reverse hampers any examination of that face. The weft yarns do not float between sections where needed by the design; instead, yarns of a particular color appear to be used only in discrete sections; when the weaving of that section is complete, the yarn is cut. There seem to be virtually no floats on the reverse; few weft yarn ends show. Condition: The ground fabric is soiled and slightly misshapen; small pieces cut from a matching fabric have been inserted as an underlay along all four edges to lessen the visual impact of the numerous small voids. *Dyeing*: Yarn dyed. *Selvages*: One section of selvage is present at one end of the textile; because it appears inside a fold, it is not visible on the obverse. One warp wide, the selvage is woven in weft-faced weave. Other: The outermost warp is double, a circumstance that identifies it as the selvage. All wefts turn around this warp.

[MWG]

1   Phoenix 1993, p. 109, no. 20; Zhou 1987, pp. 314–316; New York 1989, n.p., fig. 73; San Francisco 1983, p. 171, no. 111.

2   Pal and Meech-Pekarik 1988, p. 257. For illustrations of such covers, or curtains, in use, see Pal and Meech-Pekarik 1988, p. 259, fig. 101; Berger and Bartholomew 1995, pp. 190–205, nos. 48–61, particularly p. 190, no. 48.

3   Pal and Meech-Pekarik 1988, pp. 258, 260.

4   See Berger and Bartholomew 1995, p. 188, fig. 1; New York 1991, pp. 116–117, no. 49; Lee 1995, p. 76, fig. 11.

5   See Harvard University Art Museums 2000, p. 5, fig. 1; Hong Kong 1993, pp. 308–309, no. C110.

6   See Zhou 1987, p. 332.

7   Sample number: OxA-1846. According to representatives of the Research Laboratory for Archaeology and the History of Art, Oxford University (now Oxford Authentication Ltd.), on the basis of radiocarbon tests, this textile can be assigned to the period 1440–1625 with sixty eight per cent confidence or to the period 1420–1650 with ninety five per cent confidence. Results of the radiocarbon tests are published in Spink and Son 1989, pp. 29, 162, no. 27. Despite the results of the radiocarbon tests, this textile cannot date as early as the Ming dynasty. The exact reason for the early date suggested by the test results is unknown. One possibility is that the conclusions drawn from the test results are simply wrong; that is, that the actual date lies not within the "ninety five per cent confidence" range with which the 1420–1650 date was advanced but within the "five per cent confidence" range for which no dates were advanced. (In statistical interpretation—which, in fact, underlies all conclusions drawn from the raw results of radiocarbon tests—such small percentages cannot be ignored, let alone summarily dismissed, no matter how seemingly insignificant.) Another possibility is that even though the test results, and the conclusions drawn from them, technically are accurate, either the textile or the sample taken from it was contaminated such that the test results are skewed. Yet another possibility—unlikely though not impossible—is that although it was woven in the eighteenth century, during the Qianlong reign, this textile was woven with old yarn—that is, with yarn perhaps made as early as the Ming dynasty. Since, in effect, radiocarbon tests determine when a material was last living, such tests performed on a sample of silk essentially determine when the silkworm spun the silk for its cocoon, not when the fibers were spun into yarn, let alone when the yarn was woven into fabric. Thus, the test results, and the conclusions drawn from them, though accurate, could be indicating the date of the yarn. (Though seldom, if ever, mentioned, the working hypothesis underlying radiocarbon testing of textiles is that the fabric—from which the specimen to be tested was removed—was woven with newly spun yarn; under those circumstances, the date of the yarn is nearly the same as that of the woven fabric. If old yarn is used, then the results of the radiocarbon tests point to the date of the yarn, not to the date the finished fabric was woven.) It is seldom possible to explain why scientific tests fail to accord with sound data gleaned from other sources; this is no less true in conservation science than in medicine, where the interpretation of laboratory tests, though usually accurate, cannot be guaranteed to be one hundred per cent accurate.

8   AEDTA inventory number 2603. See Riboud et al. 1996, n.p., pl. 22; for a detail of the same cover, see Myers 1989, p. 140, fig. 10.

9   See Pal and Meech-Pekarik 1988, p. 242, pl. 74a–e.

10   See Berger and Bartholomew 1995, p. 190, no. 48.

14

[Detail]

Qing dynasty, 17th–early 18th century
   Silk *kesi* tapestry; dyed polychrome silk yarns and gold-wrapped yarns in weft-faced
   tabby-weave fabric utilizing the *kesi* tapestry technique to create representational
   patterns; minimal painted details
H. 32.3 cm; W. 21.5 cm, including selvages

Three panels, each with a dark blue silk ground, depict refined groupings of flowers and [89] antiques. Panel A represents a branch of blossoming prunus in a vase of square section, standing on a small base. The vase is woven in shades suggesting blue-and-white porcelain. The vessel's shape, however, as well as its ring handles, reflect a bronze prototype. Placed to the side of the tall vase is a squat three-footed vessel, probably a bronze water pot. Emerging from the pot is a *ruyi* shaped form which adorns a ladle for dipping the water. This tripod, or *ding* shaped vessel, is typical of Ming dynasty bronzes associated with the Xuande era (1426–1435).[1] Panel B depicts three elements. At lower left, a footed rectangular tray holds two cups for tea or wine. At lower right, a squat bowl holds an orchid. Above and just left of center is a bowl containing three fragrant fruits of the type called finger citron (*foshou*; Buddha's hand fruits) displayed on a high pedestal of red lacquer. Panel C depicts a large porcelain vase of *meiping* shape holding a flowering branch. The surface of the vase has the appearance of the highly admired *guan* ware of the Song dynasty, an effect achieved by delicately painting in details to simulate a crackled white or pale celadon glaze. The shoulders of the vase are fitted with ring handles held by abstract animal masks, another reference to antiquity. The vessel is supported by a stand, woven in gold thread, perhaps to imitate gilt wood. Microscopy reveals the character of these yarns wrapped with gold applied to a substrate of paper. Completing the composition are two small rabbits on a banana leaf. The veins of the leaf are, like the glaze of the *meiping*, rendered by painting.

These three *kesi* panels were probably part of a larger series representing arrangements of flowers and antiquities for New Year celebrations.[2] Each scene has a combination of motifs which would have suggested the refinement of a scholar's art collection while at the same time conveying good wishes and seasonal felicity. The plum blossom, often called one of the three friends of winter, might be taken as a celebration of the New Year. The finger citron (*Citrus medica* var. *sarcodactylis*) was also a New Year's motif, as it was used to make a fragrant offering for the New Year holiday.[3] The cymbidium orchid (*lanhua*) can be symbolic of spring, the first season of the year.[4] The flowering branch of Panel C may be osmanthus (*guihua*), associated with the moon festival and lunar legends.[5] The association with the moon may be the reason for the appearance of the rabbits. More likely, however, they form a reference to the animal symbols of the zodiac and particularly the year of the rabbit.[6]

The isolation of these objects and their careful arrangement against the blue ground seems reminiscent of the color woodblock print compositions that rose to prominence in China in the seventeenth century. Late Ming and early Qing prints often depicted scenes of antiques and flowers in auspicious arrangements.[7] A close parallel to the elegant simplicity of the displays in this series of textiles is found in the woodblock prints of the *Luoxuan biangu jian pu* (The Wisteria Studio Album of Stationery Decorated with Ancient and Modern Designs), preface dated 1626.[8] The album included chapters on scholars' objects and antiquities (*bowu*) and on cut flowers (*zhezeng*). It has been identified as the earliest surviving example of multiple-block color printing.[9] This tradition ultimately gave rise to the *surimono* print compositions of eighteenth-nineteenth century Japan. In these privately commissioned and highly refined Japanese prints, New Year's symbolism appeared in ever more complex and subtle forms.[10] The three Clague textile panels may provide insight into the Chinese roots of that remarkable development.

Although the panels are of a size and format suitable to have been leaves in an album, they may also have formed a part of a series for architectural decoration, either mounted on the wall itself or in a wooden screen.[11] The antiquities motif, called *bogu* (collected antiquities),[12] became widespread in textiles of the eighteenth century, but the style shifted towards more complex compositions crowded with scholar's objects, antiques, and auspicious flowers.[13] The motif is represented in eighteenth century textiles, both embroidery and *kesi* tapestry, preserved in the palace collection.[14] The Clague series appears to be a precursor of these. Its close resemblance to seventeenth century compositions in prints and other media support a date in the early years of Qing.

[CB]

Publications: Urban Council, Hong Kong, and the Oriental Ceramic Society of
Hong Kong in association with the Liaoning Provincial Museum. *Jinxiu luoyi qiao tiangong / Heavens' Embroidered Cloths: One Thousand Years of Chinese Textiles*. Exh. cat., Hong Kong Museum of Art.
Hong Kong, 1995, pp. 103–105, cat. no. 16b–d.

Technical analysis

Warp: Tan silk; Z twist; 2-ply. Count: 24 yarns per centimeter. Condition: Many warp yarns have formed loops on fabric surface as they have been pulled somewhat from the fabric weave. This is found on all three textiles. *Weft*: 1) Polychrome silk; Z twist; no ply (bundled yarns not twisted together). Count: Variable, 23 to 28 yarns per centimeter. The weft yarns are much heavier than the warp yarns, perhaps 4 times as thick. 2) Bundled pale yellow silk yarns wrapped with gold adhered to a substrate; Z twist; no ply (bundled yarns not twisted together). Count: 21 yarns per centimeter. Other: This yarn appears only in the stand for the vase (textile C). The gold wrapped yarns were examined under high power optical microscope. Under high magnification, some of the metallic yarns do not appear to be gold but a gray metallic yarn. *Weave*: Kesi. Textile is woven in the tapestry technique (weft faced tabby) with slit joins. Where the gold yarns are found, the weaving is one pass of gold yarns and one pass of non-metallic yarns. *Dyeing*: Yarn dyed. *Selvages*: Weave: Weft faced tabby. Width: 1 centimeter wide on all six selvages. Location: on both sides of each textile. The weft yarns wrap around the outermost warp (which is a double yarn) and continue into the next shed.

Embellishments

Ink details (textile C), depicting light brown veins on the leaf and gray crackled lines on the ceramic vase.

Commentary

Leaf C was examined under optical microscope at Arizona State University's Center for Solid State Science, 28 October 1998.

[MWG]

14

[A]

14

[B]

14

[C]

1   For example, Phoenix 1993, cat. nos. 25 and 29.

2   The panels were separated at some point in their history. Panel C
    was purchased by Amy Clague in December 1992; in July of 1993,
    she purchased panels A and B, reuniting three of what was probably
    an eight-panel set.

3   Bartholomew 1985, p. 32. It can also be read as a rebus for
    happiness and longevity.

4   Asian Art Museum 1985, n. p., cat. no. 9.

5   Asian Art Museum 1985, n.p., cat. no. 45.

6   For a similar interpretation of a tapestry in the National Palace
    Museum collection, see National Palace Museum 1970, text volume,
    p. 33 (English text).

7   For examples of 17th century prints of these subjects,
    see Vedlich 1979, pp. 70–71, 78–79, 80–81, 84–85, 92–96, all prints
    from the series called the Kaempfer series after the German doctor
    who brought them back to Europe in the late 17th century
    (pp. 10–11).

8   New York 1987, cat. no. 27, and p. 161.

9   New York 1987, p. 60.

10 On *surimono* and their New Year's symbolism, see Mirviss 1995.

11 A 19th century wooden screen of six folds, with textiles woven in the
    18th century, including a series of antiques and flowers on a dark
    blue ground, was offered for sale recently at Sotheby's, New York,
    sale number 7508 (September 20, 2000), lot no. 37. A pair of
    hanging scrolls on the *bogu* theme, now in the National Palace
    Museum collection, are described as former screen panels
    (NPM, text volume, p. 33 [English text]).

12 See Feng Zhao 1999, pp. 238–241, and fig. 08.00h.

13 For an example of the motif used as an elaborate border,
    see Hong Kong 1995, pp. 108–109, cat. no. 18.

14 See National Palace Museum 1970, text volume, pls. 83–84 and
    fig. 111; also text volume, pls. 79–80. A related work is illustrated
    in Huang 1987, cat. no. 175, pp. 84 and 176.

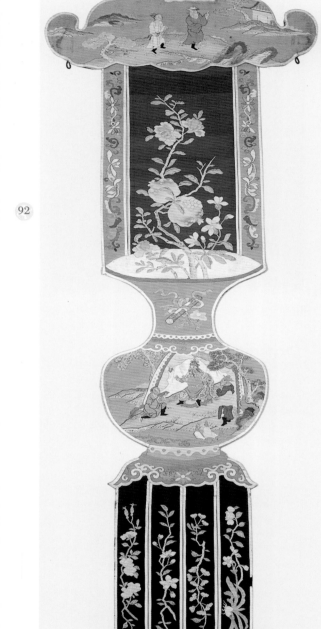

15

[Front]　　　　　　　　　　　　　　　　[Back]

15 Eight Banners with Flowers and Narrative Scenes, including Scenes from *The Romance of the Western Chamber*

Chinese, Qing dynasty, late 17th to early 18th century
Silk *kesi* tapestry and painting in ink and colors on silk; dyed polychrome silk yarns and gold-wrapped yarns in weft-faced tabby-weave fabric utilizing the *kesi* tapestry technique to create representational patterns; tabby-weave openwork silk ground for painting; additional fabric of dyed blue silk yarns in a 4/1 satin weave
H. 107 cm; W. 36 cm (max)

This remarkable set of eight banners[1] is constructed of *kesi* tapestry on the obverse and painted silk fabrics on the reverse. The weavers created the main panels of the obverse including the side streamers and the four below in one continuous weaving, so that warp threads run all the way from the top of the blue panel to the pointed bottom of each streamer. The upper field of decoration, woven in *kesi* of identical characteristics, was produced and mounted separately. A narrow satin binding was stitched around all the edges. The reverse of each banner is constructed of two fabrics. The main fabric is a fine silk ground of undyed yarns woven in a minute open-work weave revealed by microscopy (see detail and technical analysis below). These are painted in ink and colors with subjects and formats to complement the obverse of the banners. A woven silk braid embellishes the edges of the main fields of painted decoration. Blue satin fabric is used to line the backs of the two side and four bottom streamers. This satin lining is embellished with patterns in black ink. Throughout the *kesi* weavings on the obverse, gold-wrapped silk yarns are woven in to highlight such details as the veins of leaves, the ornamental borders of the vases (suggesting gilded areas on bronze or porcelain), and elements in the narrative scenes.

The upper segment of each banner is formed in the shape of the *ruyi* (a cloud-shaped form of auspicious symbolism). On the obverse these are faced with weavings in *kesi*, each showing a narrative scene in a landscape setting. Each has two figures; four show scenes of combat, four show scenes of two figures interacting, usually one figure shown as if in supplication to the other. In the large field of decoration, each banner has a shape imitating a vase decorated with narrative scenes. Each vase has a different selection of flowers arranged with one large and one small grouping portrayed against a light background to suggest the flaring lip of the vase and a dark blue ground to suggest openness beyond. Included among the flowers are pomegranate with osmanthus, peony with chrysanthemum, camellia, hibiscus with begonia, lotus, prunus with camellia, and orchid with fungus and bamboo. These combinations may have suggested specific good wishes. For example, the peony, associated with wealth, is flanked below by chrysanthemums, symbolic of scholarly accomplishment.[2] The side streamers for each of these central panels are woven in *kesi* technique to create ornamental floral patterns, creating a decorative frame around the representational motifs. These are symmetrically reversed to frame each panel.

15

[Fronts]

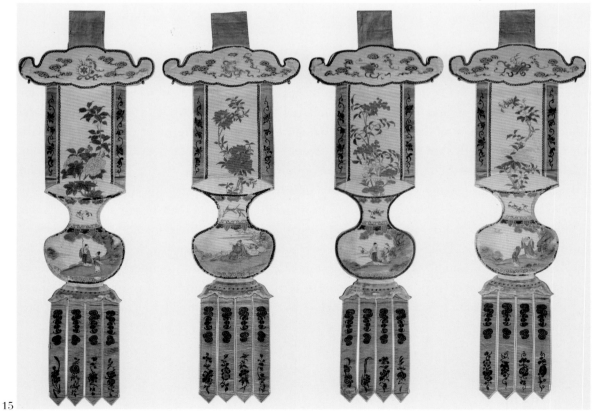

15

[Backs]

Each vase depicted on the obverse of the banners has a decorative scheme, including auspicious symbols on the neck, narrative scenes on the belly, and ornamental patterning at the foot and pedestal of the vessel. A border of *ruyi* shapes divides the fields for narrative and ornamental decoration. Depicted on the necks of each vase are the attributes of the eight immortals,[3] each adorned with ribbons. These are (right to left): the gourd of Li Tieguai, the scroll and flowers of Lan Caihe, the flute of Han Xiangzi, the bamboo tube and rod of Zhang Guolao, the castanets of Cao Guojiu, the fan of Zhongli Quan, the sword of Lu Dongbin, and the flowering branch of He Xiangu. These symbols would evoke the delightful legends of the immortals while conveying wishes for longevity. Descending from the elaborate base of each vessel are four streamers, each depicting flowers and plants against a black ground, all delicately woven in *kesi* technique. There are no repeated patterns and each streamer may have as many as three plants depicted. Each forms a tiny composition of its own with cut branches stretching out vertically to fill the space. One, for example, depicts the pine, bamboo, and prunus, a combination of motifs known as the "Three Friends of Winter," often found in painting and poetry. It may be presumed that the other motifs and combinations were similarly chosen for their symbolic associations.

On the belly of each vase is depicted a narrative scene, each with several figures in an architectural or landscape setting. These have enough detail to suggest specifically the illustration of the famous Yuan drama, *Xixiang ji*, best known in English as *The Romance of the Western Chamber*.[4] A tentative interpretation of the scenes (right to left) may be made as follows:

> The rebel General Sun Biao, the "Flying Tiger," attacking the Pujiu Monastery (Temple of Universal Salvation) makes his threat to the abbot and Student Zhang (Zhang Gong, Zhang Junrui). The abbot holds a fly whisk and wears an ecclesiastical hat. Viewers of these banners would readily have known that Student Zhang has already fallen in love with Cui Yingying (Oriole) who was taking shelter with her family within the monastery. Yingying's mother has promised her hand in marriage to anyone who can save them from the rebels who now have the temple under siege.

> A letter arrives asking General Du for help. The General is shown in his campaign tent. The young monk from Pujiu Monastery delivers the letter from Student Zhang asking his friend the General to save the temple from General Sun, "the Flying Tiger," who threatens to abduct Cui Yingying (Oriole).[5] At the lower edge of the scene, banners carried in procession hint of the General's large army.

> In the assault on the Pujiu Monastery by the rebel General Sun, General Du on the white horse routs the rebel leader. Viewers would remember that since Student Zhang had saved them from the rebel general, Madame Cui should allow him to marry Yingying. She reneged, however, claiming Yingying had already been betrothed to a loathsome cousin, Zheng Heng.

> Student Zhang and Yingying (Oriole) meet, attended by Hongniang (Crimson). Student Zhang's servant rushes in.

> Madame Cui, having discovered the trysting of the lovers, chastises Hongniang (Crimson), Yingying's servant and go-between for the lovers. Behind her chair stands a screen decorated with an ink landscape. In the drama, this is a pivotal scene in which Madame Cui relents and promises Yingying's hand in marriage to Student Zhang, but only if he succeeds in the civil service exams.

> Student Zhang travels to the capital to take the civil service exam. His servant bears his lute and his books on a carrying pole.[6]

> Student Zhang dreams of Yingying (Oriole) while on his way to the Capital. He sits at a desk in the inn. His dream is portrayed by the scrolling mist of white that envelops the figure of Yingying.

> Student Zhang appears with Hongniang (Crimson) the go-between and Madame Cui's nephew (Zheng Heng), a caricature of bad taste, shown here hiding his face with a fan. This scene denotes the end of the drama when Zheng Heng's plot to marry Yingying (Oriole) fails. Student Zhang, now successful in the exams and with a high official appointment, has foiled the plot—with Crimson's help—and at last marries Yingying.

Narrative scenes in these textiles, like those on ceramics of the seventeenth century, especially the Transitional period (1620–1683),[7] drew inspiration from contemporary illustrated novels and plays. They do not match extant woodblock prints exactly, but probably adapted motifs and conventions from them. The scenes in these eight banners may have been inspired by woodblock prints in the many illustrated editions of the *Xixiang ji* and other plays and novels. However, the designers ingeniously incorporated elements of the narrative into a context of landscape and architectural details providing consistency from one banner to the next. Distant mountains and garden rocks are woven in shades of blue alternating with green and white, grassy slopes are woven in green, and stylized clouds are swirls of white banded with blue. The background of each scene is a light red, probably faded from a brighter shade.

Studies of dramatic illustrations on porcelain have shown that the most dramatic moments of the story may be avoided in favor of scenes which suggest the action more obliquely.[8] That is certainly the case in these textiles. At issue was good taste and a wish to avoid overtly erotic scenes, as well as a desire to create ingenious and subtle references to the story.[9] Although some parallels with woodblock print illustrations can be found, the illustrative program seen here was probably the design of professionals working directly with the textile producers and may have drawn as much on a tradition of illustration in *kesi* as on the printed editions then available.[10] There were regional traditions in book illustration as well, and these should be taken into account in future studies of dramatic narratives in textiles.

An interest in drama is prevalent throughout the front of the banners. The upper scenes may be episodes from the *Water Margin (Shuihu zhuan)* or the *Romance of the Three Kingdoms (Sanguo zhi)*.[11] Even the theme of the eight immortals alluded to here by their attributes relates to theatrical performance, for in the seventeenth century stories of the eight immortals were performed as dramas especially for birthday celebrations.[12] These themes resonate with the subtext of references to scholarly accomplishment and success in the civil service examinations.

The reverse of the banners are painted, again using the vase shape and cut flowers shown as if arranged in the vessels. On the *ruyi*-shaped panels are depicted the eight auspicious objects (*bajixiang*, see number 5) among clouds and bats. On the belly of the vases are scenes of scholars with boy attendants, either in their studios or traveling in landscapes.[13] On the neck of each vase is a leafy or flowering branch. Decoration on the vases themselves is suggested by painted details similar to the woven ornamentation on the obverse. The blue satin linings have symmetrical black ink silhouettes of scrolling blossoms on the side streamers and bats and clouds on the upper part of the bottom streamers. The lower segment of each streamer bears a remarkable series of silhouetted floral motifs, each portraying a different elongated branch of flowers and leaves.

The construction of the banners with a top portion of either triangular or cloud shape, a long rectangular panel forming a central focal point, two side streamers attached to it at top and bottom, and four loose streamers dangling below is a type ultimately based on the sort of banner used in Buddhist worship,[14] when it would be hung in a temple or carried in procession. Banners of long narrow proportion, adorned with side streamers and end streamers, were used for inscriptions during the Ming and the Qing, as documented in paintings[15] as well as in surviving examples.[16] The present set of banners, although descended from this type of religious banner, employs pictorial images of a secular nature and combines shapes and symbols in a witty and complex manner that reflects the scholar's taste. This and the nature of the imagery suggest a domestic interior as the original setting for these banners. The eight banners probably played a decorative role among interior furnishings of a gentry household. They may have been used within the framework of a hardwood folding screen,[17] so that the banners would be visible from both sides.

Dramatic illustration in porcelain reached its high point in the late seventeenth century.[18] At the same time, the popularity of *The Romance of the Western Chamber* also reached its peak. A reaction against the *Xixiang ji's* erotic content, seen as licentious during the Qianlong era, may have contributed to a decline of dramatic illustration in textiles, ceramics, and other decorative arts. This and stylistic evidence support a date for this remarkable set of textiles within the early Qing period.

[CB]

Publications: Urban Council, Hong Kong, and the Oriental Ceramic Society of Hong Kong in association with the Liaoning Provincial Museum. *Jinxiu luoyi qiao tiangong / Heavens' Embroidered Cloths: One Thousand Years of Chinese Textiles*. Exh. cat., Hong Kong Museum of Art. Hong Kong, 1995, pp. 98–101, cat. no. 15.

Technical analysis

Note: The eight banners differ in motifs but have the same technical characteristics. One type of fabric (*kesi*) appears on the obverse, two fabrics on the reverse of each banner. The following analysis is based on examination of banner with the battle scene (third from right).

Obverse

Warp: Tan silk; no apparent twist; 2-ply. Count: 20 yarns per centimeter. Very fine in diameter. *Weft*: Foundation: 1) Polychrome silk; no apparent twist; no ply (bundled yarns not twisted together). Count: 40 yarns per centimeter. Other: Approximately 4 times thicker than warp yarns. 2) Pink (faded red) silk wrapped with gold; Z twist; no ply (bundled yarns not twisted together). *Weave*: *Kesi*. Textile is woven in the tapestry technique (weft faced tabby) with slit joins. There is eccentric weaving in the curves. *Dyeing*: Yarn dyed. *Selvages*: none remaining.

Embellishments

Ink details throughout the *kesi* pictorial motifs. *Binding*: Location: around all edges of banners. *Fiber*: Silk. *Weave*: Satin. *Color*: Off-white.

Reverse: fabric 1

Warp: Off-white silk; no apparent twist; no ply (bundled yarns not twisted together). Count: 20 yarns per centimeter. *Weft*: Off-white silk; no apparent twist; no ply (bundled yarns not twisted together). Count: 32 yarns per centimeter. *Weave*: Tabby weave in a pattern of openwork. *Dyeing*: Undetermined. Under high power magnification, the fabric appears undyed because of dark spots which could indicate foreign matter that may be covered with color if dyed.

Commentary

The weave of the off-white fabric was examined under the optical microscope at Arizona State University's Center for Solid State Science on 28 October 1998. The tabby weave pattern is two warps close to one another and then a space, repeated over the entire fabric. Remarkably, the warp yarns have not shifted and filled the spaces. A photo records the weave pattern. (Note: The vertical yarns were designated as the warp but this could not be verified because there are no selvages.)

Reverse: fabric 2

Warp: Blue silk; slight Z twist; single ply. Count: 24 yarns per centimeter. *Weft*: Blue silk; no apparent twist; no ply (bundled yarns not twisted together). Count: 24 yarns per centimeter. *Weave*: 4/1 satin. *Dyeing*: Yarn dyed. *Selvages*: none remaining.

Embellishments

Painted in colors and ink. *Braid*: 0.5 cm wide, silk, black flat braid and blue flat braid. Both with a woven white and yellow design. All banners have braid in the same location but two banners have blue braid in the oval shaped section while the other six banners have black braid.

[MWG]

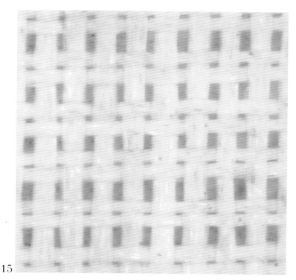

15

[Detail: optical microscopy, back]

15

[Detail]

1   The banners were for a time separated into two sets. Amy Clague reunited the set by purchasing four banners in December 1992 and the other four in February 1993.

2   For specific analysis of botanical motifs and their use as rebuses in Chinese art, see Bartholomew 1985.

3   These form a set called the *an baxian* (parallel to the *bajixiang* discussed in number 5). Although the attributes vary, a useful description of them is found in Melbourne 1988, pp. 44–45.

4   The play composed by Yuan playwright Wang Shifu (fl. 1297–1307) was based on a novel by the Tang poet Yuan Zhen (785–804). For a standard translation of the drama, see Hsiung 1935. A new translation (Wang 1991) includes an appendix (Yao 1991) discussing the woodblock illustrations of the Hongzhi period edition of the drama. Most of the surviving editions of the drama date between 1550 and 1700. Many noted artists provided illustrations, including Qian Gu (1508–after 1574) and Chen Hongshou (1599–1652).

5   A similar scene of General Du in his tent is shown in a woodblock print of the late Yuan-early Ming period. See Yao 1991, fig. 31.

6   For related scenes in woodblock prints see Yao 1991, figs. 9 and 16.

7   On blue-and-white porcelains of this period see New York 1983 (in particular, cat. no. 41, pp. 94–97, a vase with illustrations of the *Xixiang ji*) and New York 1995.

8   Clunas 1981–2, pp. 75–76.

9   Delbanco 1983, pp. 20–23, describes the inventiveness of the Min Qiji album now in Cologne, datable to 1640.

10 This situation may parallel that in ceramics, described by Clunas 1981–2, pp. 74-75.

11 The illustration on porcelain of these older narratives is discussed by Hsu 1986, pp. 29–33.

12 Hsu 1986, p. 34.

13 One of these scenes, a winter landscape with snowy mountains, seems appropriate as a closing scene in a series, just as a winter scene often closes an album of paintings. However, the narrative scenes on the obverse of the banners would not make sense if the position of that banner were shifted. This may suggest that the banners were hung in groups of four, so that the winter scene would be at the left (or end, if reading right to left as Chinese texts are read) of one of the two groups.

14 For an example from the Tang dynasty now in the Los Angeles County Museum of Art (accession number AC 1996.129.1), see Gluckman 2000, pp. 90-91, figs. 1–1a.

15 A Buddhist painting of the Ming dynasty (illustrated in Lawrence, KS 1994, plate 17, p. 287 and cat. no. 31) shows two such inscribed banners, each with a line of characters in gold on a dark blue ground.

16 A set of four banners, woven in *kesi* technique, each banner with one line of characters, has been dated to the Qianlong period. The set is in The Newark Museum (accession number 41.2035 A–D); see New York 1980 a, cat. no. 42, pp. 64–65. A set of eight banners, graduated in length, is visible in an early twentieth century photograph taken in one of the temples within the Forbidden City, Beijing. The decoration on these is not visible in the photograph, but the construction is similar. See Sirén 1926, vol. II, pl. 150.

17 For an example of the type of hardwood screen that might have held such textiles, see Bruce 1991, cat. no. 57, pp. 144–145.

18 Clunas 1981–2, p. 79, places this peak in the late 17th–early 18th century; Hsu 1986, dates the *Xixiang ji* representations in porcelain to the second half of the transitional period (1620–ca. 1683).

16

Chinese, Qing dynasty, 18th century
  Slit tapestry of wool and linen with silk highlights; dyed polychrome wool and
  silk yarns in weft-faced tabby-weave fabric utilizing the tapestry technique to create
  representational patterns
H. 111.5 cm; W. 73 cm

This large panel depicts a view of distant mountains framed by the twisting branches of a pomegranate tree on one side and the prominent blossoms of a hydrangea bush on the other. Lilies, roses, camellia, and garden rocks form foreground motifs while a stream meanders through the center toward a distant mountain. A band of mist, suggested by a horizontal band of light colored yarns, partially obscures a grove of trees. Five bats fly about in a sky that darkens gradually to a deep blue at the top of the panel. Although the scene depicted can be appreciated simply as a landscape, the motifs were no doubt selected for their auspicious symbolism. The pomegranate, for example, may be seen, even in the most general of terms, as a symbol of many wishes fulfilled. The five bats (*wufu*) refer specifically to five blessings: old age, wealth, health, love of virtue, and a peaceful death.[1]

With the warp running horizontal in the work, the weavers have used the tapestry technique and subtle shifts in color to create an effect of modeling in light and shade. This modeling, with the low horizon and the deep perspective, sets this landscape apart from most Chinese landscape tapestries that usually juxtapose contrasting bright colors for a jewel-like effect or, as in number 17, imitate the textural brush strokes of Chinese painting. Here the branches of trees and the surfaces of rocks are carefully shaded, shadows seem to be cast by the foreground rocks, and minute gradations of color suggest the deepening color of the sky at dusk.

Similar to *kesi* (silk tapestry) but apparently intended to have a European appearance, this example was woven in a modified technique (see Technical Analysis below) to suggest the flavor of European tapestries. Notably, wool is the primary fiber and the warp yarns are linen. Silk fibers are also woven into the fabric. Wool and linen fibers were typically used in European tapestries of the seventeenth and eighteenth centuries.

The Qianlong emperor commissioned European style palaces to be built at his Yuanmingyuan palace; construction took place from 1747 to 1759, with an addition probably in 1768.[2] We can infer that tapestries graced the interiors of those buildings along with other furnishings in European style, for in 1767, when Qianlong was presented a set of tapestries made at Beauvais based on designs by French artist Francois Boucher (1703–1770), he commissioned the building of a new palace for their display.[3] It is thus tempting to suggest that the Clague landscape panel was intended for use in this European style setting.

101

Studies of the Yuanmingyuan have emphasized that although the buildings were designed by European missionary artists—primarily Giuseppe Castiglione (1688–1766), Michel Benoist (1715–1774), Jean-Denis Attiret (1702–1768), and Ignatius Sichelbarth (1708–1780)—the designs were a fusion of European and Chinese styles. A similar process had already taken place in painting among missionary artists at court, above all in the work of Castiglione.[4] That is, European elements, particularly *chiaroscuro* modeling and some aspects of Western perspective, were combined with Chinese formats (hanging scrolls, handscrolls, and albums), Chinese materials (silk or paper ground, ink and water-based pigments), Chinese subject matter, and aspects of the representational style of painting which had flourished at court during the Song and early Ming periods. The European style of the Qing court was thus, like Europe's Chinoiserie, a mixture of traditions. A similar mixing occurs in the Clague landscape tapestry. For example, the motifs are drawn wholly from the Chinese tradition (bats, flowering trees, and garden rocks) and do not include the human figures almost always present in European tapestries. Yet, as in Castiglione's paintings, the Chinese subjects are presented in a technique which renders the work exotic in flavor but still palatable to Chinese court taste.

Like eighteenth-century enamels, glass, and other decorative arts, tapestries were an aspect of European art known in China, but were also a medium through which European artists expressed their imaginary views of the distant empire of Cathay. The French manufactories of tapestries at Beauvais and Aubusson textile factories produced Chinoiserie tapestries during the late seventeenth and eighteenth centuries, including a set made at Beauvais called the *History of the Empire of China*.[5] German and British textiles also reflect this interest.[6]

Unusual as this work seems within the context of Qing textiles, it does have links to tapestries surviving in the collection of the Palace Museum, Beijing. For example, two works,[7] both with poetic inscriptions, employ strong shading and a similar gradation of color in the sky. However, their compositions are closely based on traditional Chinese paintings and lack the pronounced suggestion of spatial recession of the Clague landscape.

[CB]

Publications: Claudia Brown, "The Amy S. Clague Collection of Chinese Textiles,"
                      Orientations 31, no. 2 (February 2000), p. 40, figs. 12 and 12a;
                      Urban Council, Hong Kong, and the Oriental Ceramic Society of
                      Hong Kong in association with the Liaoning Provincial Museum.
                      *Jinxiu luoyi qiao tiangong / Heavens' Embroidered Cloths: One Thousand
                      Years of Chinese Textiles*. Exh. cat., Hong Kong Museum of Art.
                      Hong Kong, 1995, pp. 90–91, cat. no. 11.

103

16
[Detail]

16
[Detail]

Technical analysis

Warp: Dark tan colored linen; S twist; 2-ply. Count: 15 yarns per centimeter. *Weft*: Foundation: 1) Throughout the bottom two-thirds of the textile: polychrome wool; S twist; 2-ply, Z. Count: 30 yarns per centimeter. 2) In the blue sky, the tan section of sky, the gray and brown flowers, and gray part of the fruit: gray, gray-brown, and blue silk; slight Z twist; single ply. Count: 30 weft yarns per centimeter. *Weave*: Slit tapestry. It is a weft faced tabby with slit joins. Textile is woven in the European technique of linen warp with wool and silk weft yarns. The weft yarns do not pass on the reverse side from one area to where the yarn is needed next (another European technique). *Dyeing*: Yarn dyed. *Selvages*: none remaining.

Commentary

The textile has been cut from a larger piece.

[MWG]

1   Bartholomew 1985, p. 28.

2   Pirazzoli-t'Serstevens 1988, p. 62.

3   Pirazzoli-t'Serstevens 1988, p. 63. See also Jarry 1981, pp. 28–32.
    Tapestries made at Beauvais were often used as diplomatic gifts by
    the French king in the late 17th and early 18th centuries.
    See Gastinel-Coural 1996, pp. 460–461. In a letter of 1787 written
    by Father Bourgeois, apparently the same set of tapestries was
    referred to as the product of Gobelins, and the same identification
    was made by 19th century observers. See Malone 1934, pp. 160
    and 184.

4   For a summary of Castiglione's early experiences in developing a
    blended style of painting that appealed to the Qing emperors,
    see Rogers 1988, pp. 141–152. A recent study (Berinstein 1999)
    suggests that European tapestries may have been a source
    Castiglione drew from for his portraits of Qianlong.

5   One of this series is illustrated in Berlin 1985, p. 120,
    plate 111 (cat. no. 9/36). For additional examples of Chinoiserie
    tapestries from Beauvais, see in the same source, p. 97, pl. 93;
    pp. 177 and 359, pl. 168 and cat. no. 13/41, and pp. 317–318,
    cat. no. 10/54. And from Aubusson, pp. 229–230, cat. no. 4/39;
    and pp. 324–325, cat. no. 11/29. All of these are described
    as wool and silk.

6   Riccardi-Cubitt 1996, p. 167.

7   Huang 1987, cat. nos. 165 and 172.

Chinese, Qing dynasty, Qianlong reign, 1736–1795
  Silk *kesi* tapestry; dyed polychrome and undyed silk yarns in weft-faced tabby-weave
  fabric utilizing the *kesi* tapestry technique to create representational patterns and
  calligraphy; minor painted details on the first leaf
each leaf: H. 38 cm; W. 54 cm

This album of twelve leaves was commissioned by the imperial court. It opens with a woven 105
landscape depicting the famous scenery of West Lake near Hangzhou, and continues with eleven
double leaves of the Qianlong emperor's poetry on the same theme woven in clerical script.

The cover of the album is a dark hardwood (*zitan*) with borders of silver wire inlaid in a keyfret
pattern. The title, *Imperial Poems on West Lake Scenery*, its characters in clerical script, is
inlaid in turquoise blue enamel and surrounded by an inlaid silver border depicting two dragons
encircled by clouds and stretched out along each side as if reaching for a flaming pearl at the
top. A simplified representation of mountains and waves appears below.

The first leaf of the album is woven to represent a panoramic view of a lake and surrounding
hills. In the foreground a path leads up the mountain past a lakeside villa and other garden
architecture of open pavilions and large sculptural stones of the style called Taihu rocks, which
have distinctive eroded surfaces and large perforations. These rocks take their name from Lake
Tai, near Suzhou, where limestone rocks were traditionally allowed to erode under water to
achieve interesting effects. A larger building on a stone foundation is actually set out into
the water, connected to an angled bridge. Beyond is a stairway for disembarking by boat.
Blossoming fruit trees denote a springtime scene, perhaps a further suggestion of the ideal qualities
of this scenic spot. The pictorial scene is bordered by a wide blue border which is woven
continuously with the pictorial motifs. The *kesi* technique successfully creates a landscape of
minute detail, and beyond that, it simulates the effect of brushwork in the orthodox manner of
Qing court painters. Although there are a few painted details, the weaver's craft is marvelously
executed in an extraordinarily fine weave of colored yarns.

The next eleven leaves are woven with vertical lines of clerical script calligraphy transcribing
poems by the Qianlong emperor on themes relating to West Lake. A broad border of blue is
woven around the four edges of each rectangular double leaf. Each group of verses is separately titled and continues for two or more double leaves. The bright blue yarns of the characters
stand out against the unbleached silk yarns of the ground. The clerical script is based on
engraved—as opposed to brush written—calligraphy of the Han dynasty (206 B.C.–A.D. 220)
and thus each stroke of each character is even in width. Each character fills an imaginary
square and the spacing of the characters is regular. The choice of the script implies a reverence
for antiquity and complements the many Arcadian references in the poems. The emperor's erudition
is also emphasized by these aspects of the album.

106

17

[Cover]

Imperial Poems on West Lake Scenery

The Qianlong emperor is said to have written more than 42,000 poems,[1] many of them inspired by the famous scenery viewed on his six Southern Inspection Tours. The emperor commissioned a series of paintings (*Nanxuntu*) to commemorate his first tour of 1751.[2] The twelve scrolls were painted by Xu Yang (active c. 1750–after 1776); the project was carried out from 1764 to 1770. The following year the volumes of the *Nanxun Shengdian (Magnificent Record of the Southern Tours)*, an illustrated woodblock printed edition of 6,700 pages, were completed. Some of the illustrations were based on an album of scenic views painted by Qian Weicheng (1720–1772). A painting by Qian or another court painter must have provided the model for the opening leaf of this album.[3]

The weaving of clerical script calligraphy in dark blue silk yarns has parallels in other works of the Qianlong era.[4] For example, a gourd-shaped *kesi* panel, mounted as a hanging scroll, is woven with blue threads transcribing a poem by the Qianlong emperor.[5] The poem is inscribed above a pictorial grouping of spring flowers. The Clague album is unusual, however, for the extent of its poems—29 stanzas—so that the calligraphy takes precedence over representational images.

107

The court also commissioned embroidered representations of this theme,[6] and *Scenes of West Lake* became a widespread theme in pictorial textiles of the nineteenth and twentieth centuries.[7]

[CB]

Publications: Claudia Brown, "The Amy S. Clague Collection of Chinese Textiles,"
                      Orientations 31, no. 2 (February 2000), p. 41, figs. 13a and 13b.

17

[Leaf B]

御製詩
湖心平眺

[Leaf C]

Leaves B and C

Gazing from the Heart of the Lake

[1] Palaces and terraces on the empty mirror-lake

Are the Isles of the Immortals, allowing visitors by sail;

Scenic mirages from outside the windows in all four directions,

With beautiful mountain layers on three sides.

Leaning on the balustrade, I gaze at fish "painting" across the water;

Rolling up bamboo curtains, I draw swallows flying low to
  tailor the wind.

Sitting there, my eyes move with boundless joy,

To take in all secluded tranquility.

[2] Nights of spring rain left at dawn;

In a forward-moving skiff, I feel as if I am in a little Isle
  of the Immortals.

A thousand layers of lush green are reflected in the water;

Cloudy hills from all directions welcome and bid farewell as I sail by.

There are no waves to startle my commoner's eye;

Lacking worldly desire, my spirit is joyful.

Light on the lake reminds me of a mirror's brightness,

The essence of purity.

[3] Trusting in the sky, I wish to dwell amid clouds; floating about,
  I wish to sail;

The palaces of Penglai are in mid-water,

With boundless views in all four directions,

And extraordinary scenery in all four seasons.

Was this mirror ever polished?

Not by a toad; [the mirror's] self-awakening emits brilliant light.

I want to call upon Zhuangzi for dialogue;

After grasping the ideas, in silence things are easily forgotten.

[4] Who said there was no space for towers and terraces?

They open on the surface of the mirror-lake.

To reach them, one must go by boat and leave worldly
  dust far behind;

When sitting, one should be like floating clouds, without
  schemes in mind.

Two peaks in the West are close to Heaven;

Three pagodas floating in the South are accompanied
  by a beautiful moon.

My white hair has increased, but my beard is still black;

I sigh over the changes between then and now.

[5] West Lake scenery is superb.

Where I am is the heart of the lake.

It is the chief of Five Officials,

Which is admired from all directions.

I often self-reflect,

Wondering who is responsible for the affairs of state.

Between diligence and laziness,

I find these thoughts hard to endure.

I calm myself with my gazing eye;

Concern is actually advantageous.

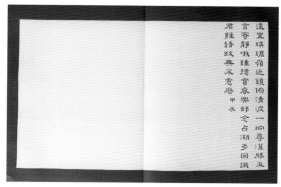

[Leaf D]

[Leaf E]

Leaves D and E

The Yiyuan (Ripple Garden, Yi Garden)

[1] Mountains are divided by Nanping Peak;
 Water fills West Lake.
 The Bamboo Pavilion and Cypress Hall
 May have been inspired by Su Shi's poem.
 Boundless magnificent scenery
 Allows me to enjoy sights from left and right with ease.
 On a boat I can absorb it all
 Because the view is exceptionally pure and beautiful.
 So with two characters I inscribe the Yi Garden
 To commemorate my first trip here.

[2] I heard that examining water requires methods;
 My famous garden is here for [examination],
 Surrounded by gates and walls.
 The moon is tossed about on the water by wind ripples;
 Flowers and woods are replicated on the mirror-lake.
 In leisure, I compose poetry in a pavilion;
 My intuitive mind wanders elsewhere
 To dwell in joyous Spring scenery.

[3] A garden next to South Hill
 Occupies ten acres on West Lake.
 Floating about, I arrive at the gate.
 Opening the studio, I attempt to paint a picture.
 I observe the appearance of geese and fish,
 And place flowers and willows on the mirror-lake.
 This requires methods similar to examining water,
 So how can one ignore this?

[4] Pure ripples are ubiquitous on West Lake.
 I encircled it to make a pond garden and wrote a
  commemorative plaque.
 An oar in hand makes it easier to enjoy the beautiful scenery,
 But my *qiyan* may not be suitable poetry.
 Birds snap up falling red flower petals,
 While fish avoid overhanging willow branches.
 Long have I considered occupying a part of the lake,
 But often I was reminded that the lake has hydraulic value.

[5] Reflections of distant green mountains are picturesque;
 Nearby they become pure ripples.
 I have always wanted to see the best clear water
 So I can use a *wuyan* poem to express my inner peace.
 Who had thought that in order to enjoy the Spring,
 I had to occupy a large part of the lake?
 Because they are reluctant to advise me,
 How can I not worry about my policies?

109

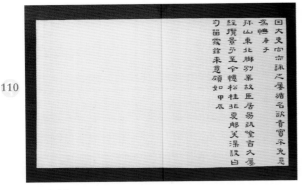

[Leaf F]

[Leaf G]

110

Leaves F and G

Yinxiang Retreat (Retreat for Chanting Fragrance)

[1] The magnificent garden called Gouliu

  Is inspired by Bai Letian's love for this state.

  Though it is a pity to let the garden decay,

  I regret more that officials are too greedy.

  If they had been as canny about people's suffering and hardship,

  It would have soothed the deepest worry in my heart.

  I sit here for a moment, not because I wish to enjoy the

    misty landscape,

  But because I wish to inscribe a poem as a reminder to protect

    my people.

[2] East of Mount Sun by the magnificent lake,

  In the Fanfu and the Gouliu Gardens, I admired Letian.

  Only the traces of ruined retreats remain,

  So I build the Yinxiang Retreat to remember the previous chapter.

  My heart's field has been cleansed pure like water;

  The fragrance I detect must be lotus,

  The gentlemen among flowers,

  Which inspires me to search for virtuous men.

[3] At the end of the ruined bridge south of Mount Sun,

  The ponds and pavilions of Fanfu Garden have long fallen into ruin.

  Who has restored it for fantastic enjoyment

  But renamed it Yinxiang from the old estate?

  After several attempts, I have not found the perfect name

  Which I could call the best one.

  In this brilliant mountain by the elegant water,

  Would it matter if I settled with the name Gouliu?

[4] This place was originally named Gouliu;

  Later I changed it to Yinxiang.

  But is it time for chanting praises to fragrance?

  There is yet water in the fields.

  Bai's pure sentences are far away;

  Fan's estate has long been in ruin.

  Green bamboo plants are symbols of high officials;

  I should praise them often.

  But if in their titles I seek substance,

  Inevitably, I am disappointed.

[5] In the northeast corner of Mount Sun

  Is the retreat of a former official.

  I have changed its name to Yinxiang long ago

  And deeply enjoy its scenery.

  But even now I think of pine and cassia,

  And if it were not Summer, there would be no lotus.

  In the place where Bai [Juyi] lingered,

  I share his thoughts.

Leaves H I and J

Xiaoyoutian Garden

[1] This wonderful place hides another small realm;

  Between Nanping Peak and the lake is boundless, elegant scenery.

  I feel I have put on a feathered garment to dwell amid clouds,

  Like an immortal transcending the dusty world.

  A few streams and brooks just had some rain;

  The gardenful of plums and willows will soon emit vapors.

  Sitting there, I attempted to write, but it was hard to get it right;

  My sentences have not sunk into emptiness, nor have I

    engaged in explaining.

[2] Hidden in an elegant, lovely, luxuriant landscape
   Is the famous Xiaoyoutian Garden.
   Bamboo shoots and purple flower buds emerge on the
      levee after thunder,
   Red petals fall, weaving by the spring and brook.
   Tranquility and ancient trees are my favorites,
   Dotting the scenery, making it slightly better than before.
   My newly built imperial studio is beautiful,
   Yet my calligraphy is inferior to that of Mad Mi [Fu].

[3] The magnificent lake leans on the foothill of Nanping Peak;
   My imperial carriage comes to Xiaoyoutian Garden.
   I recognize the city gate and old places
   Where I planted trees and built terraces.
   In the mountains filled with antique spirit, birds forget to leave;
   In the water that resonates pure music, fish enjoy the company
      of each other.
   The feeble red apricot branch I wrote about is still here;
   It happens to blossom along with garden trees.

[4] Who knows that in the deepest forest where there is no human trace
   Is the Xiaoyoutian Garden?
   My boat approaches from the magnificent lake,
   Deep into the forest,
   Where myriad flowers blossom to celebrate the Spring Festival,
   And myriad peaks are embraced by low clouds.
   Tomorrow, in the winding bamboo paths,
   I shall steal some time to linger.

[5] Xiaoyoutian Garden by Nanping Peak is my favorite;
   The view is boundless when I climb it.
   I rely on Sima Qian to interpret Yi [jing, The Book of Changes];
   My skill in *qin* [zither] cannot match that of Mad Mi [Fu].
   One hundred flowers know to celebrate the Spring Festival;
   The thousand-wood forest congeals dawn mist.
   I search for wonders amid these lush and precipitous peaks
   To see whether they can match the Chouchi Mountains.

[6] Majestic trees are like vassals
   In the famous Xiaoyoutian Garden.
   Facing the lake, a view of tranquility and purity;
   Behind it, the green mountains and clouds on a clear day.
   Why not erect high towers
   So I can take in the views with one gaze?
   In my joy I can appreciate Longjing tea,
   And chant poems following the sound of music.

[7] The Xiaoyoutian Garden that I named
   Is located in a secluded place.
   Fifteen years have gone by since my last visit.
   If during this revisit the weather becomes too hot,
   I will build halls, pavilions, and plant a forest;
   They will all be bright, reflected in the green waves.
   Entering the winding verdant paths, I come upon open views;
   West Lake presents itself as a distant mirror in my eye.
   Who said there are no more pure gatherings if one seeks
      ming (fame),
   And that *shi* (actuality) does not arrive because of one's
      joyous chanting mood?
   The human heart is but a square inch,
   Yet in it there is a Heaven that resonates.
   It exists when you participate, but vanishes if you abandon it.
   So, one's future lies in utmost respect.
   The garden far exceeds a square inch;
   Without scheme of mind, I travel in it during the day
      to chant poetry.

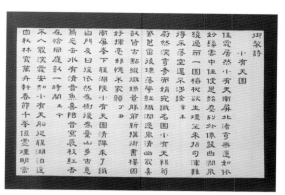

[Leaf H]

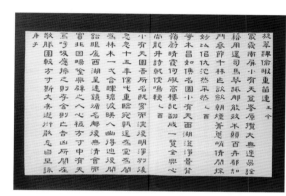

[Leaf I]

[Leaf J]

[8] When traversing the garden,
   I chant, praising beautiful views.
   When the Spring winds arrived again this time,
   I realized that I had reached another level of understanding.
   That is, inside our inch-square minds,
   Ten thousand things emerge on the spur of the moment.
   And in them, there is realm after realm;
   It is a blessing that I have this wisdom.
   But to whom may I express this idea?
   Oh, I must utterly cast off selfishness,
   Just as when Yan Yuan asked the meaning of *ren*,
   Others understood this preaching together.

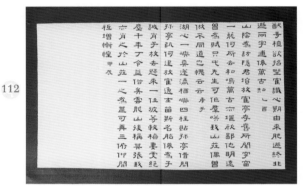

[Leaf K]

112

[Leaf L]

Leaves K and L

Crane Returns to the Plum Forest

[1] Sitting in a valley pavilion, I contemplate the ancient sage
for a moment;
The thousand-year-old Mount Sun knows that I am haughty.
Why should I await the crane's return to identify the lonely hermit?
A plum already blossoms to remember the gentleman Lin Pu.
The ancient cities Yin and Fu negotiated to return Su Shi's remains,
But kept blue mountains and green lakes behind.
Even if Ge Hong arrives from Ge Peak to boast,
A stubborn immortal may not be as worthy as a reclusive Confucian.

[2] North of Mount Sun, on the shore of the magnificent lake,
Is said to be the tomb of the recluse Mr. Lin.
He looked down upon the world and preferred to dwell
in high-mindedness,
So he did not bother with confusing mundane affairs.
The landscape has been transformed since his time,
But the phrase "crane son and plum wife" still belongs to him.
It is not that I don't want to pick up the brush,
[But] I am afraid that I have no good sentences worthy of
continuing his elegance.

[3] Sir, you are the true hermit of the past;
After traveling in Jiang and Huai, you returned alone.
So what if your crane son does not have a mother?
You would be happy to learn that your plum wife has not sought
the help of a match-maker.
Mr. Zhang of West Mountain has a skiff and a dock;
The Lu family's cloudy cliff has double-petaled blossoms.
Even today, immortals are waiting at the pavilion;
They wish to see you return on a skiff.

[4] The island in the middle of the lake is a magnificent scene;
I ask who is suited to live there.
Good sentences comprise poems on the gate of his grave.
Matching the hermit's reputation.
He planted plum trees by hand
To call upon the crane to understand his wishes.
From the beginning, many recluses may not have been true recluses,
But the term "Immortal Pu" will be known for ten thousand ages.

[5] I went north of the mountain to visit the hermit's grave;
I have heard of the Crane-releasing Pavilion.
In the giant cage of the cosmos, where did the crane go?
Its resonance of ten thousand ages soothes my mind.
There may be many high-minded virtuous men who composed prose,
[Yet] only this gentleman is worthy of company.
You may laugh at my mountain villa, which has imitated his ideas;
I am ashamed that I cannot match him.

[6] The island in the heart of the lake is truly an Isle of the Immortals
On which is the Descendant Pavilion.
You may ask where I got the idea.
Verily, the Crane-releasing Hermit left behind this name.
Having an immortal be born as a son is good;
Leaving and returning is all up to him.
He is comparable to the plum wife, who is also free of dust;
Having endured one thousand years of loneliness, she is used to it.
The Yunlong Mountains are known for Mr. Zhang
[Tianji's Crane-releasing Pavilion];
I also imitate his ideas in my mountain villa.
Having imitated them once, I am eager to repeat it,
But doing it only increases my guilt and anxiety.

[translations by An-yi Pan]

17
[Detail: leaf B]

Technical analysis

The textile part of the album is eleven double pages of calligraphy and one double page with a landscape scene. Each page has a blue woven border on the outside edges with an outer border of gold paper. All of the writing is woven into the textile. The landscape scene is a combination of woven and painted designs. The tree trunks, white and pink blossoms on the trees, the gray on the roofs, walls, and fences, the green grass, brown hills, and the blue sky are all woven designs. *Warp*: Not possible to examine because of tight weave. Count: Variable, usually 22 yarns per centimeter, and ranging up to 28 yarns per centimeter. *Weft*: White and royal blue silk; Z twist; no ply (bundled yarns not twisted together). Count: Variable, 24 to 33 yarns per centimeter. *Weave*: Kesi. Textile is woven in the tapestry technique (weft faced tabby) with slit joins. *Selvages*: none apparent.

Embellishments

Painted details of many different colors on the double page of landscape design.

Commentary

Mounted in the same way as an album of paintings with backing paper for each double leaf, and 0.25 centimeter wide paper outer border on pages.

[MWG]

1   Hummel 1943, p. 371.
2   On the Southern Inspection Tours of the Kangxi and Qianlong emperors, and their commemoration in sets of scroll paintings, see Hearn 1988.
3   For a painted album inspired by the Qianlong emperors poems from his Southern Inspection Tours, see *The Myriad Delights of Lake Shi*, by Hongwu (died 1811) in Chou 1994, cat. no. 36. Qian Weicheng painted a handscroll of West Lake scenery with poems by the Qianlong emperor and himself (cited in Sirén, vol. VII, p. 311).
4   The color blue is used for the calligraphy on many *kesi* textiles associated with the Qing court. For example, a tapestry handscroll modeled on a painting by the Ming dynasty artist Wang Guxiang is woven with inscriptions in blue (see Hong Kong 1995, cat. no. 120).
5   See National Palace Museum 1981, cat. no. 28. The Qianlong emperor's paintings were also used as models for tapestries (see National Palace Museum 1981, cat. no. 27, and Yang et al. 1983, cat. no. 46).
6   An album of ten leaves of embroidered scenes of West Lake, bearing seals of the Qianlong, Jiaqing and later Qing emperors, is in the National Palace Museum, Taiwan. See National Palace Museum 1981, cat. no. 39.
7   For examples, see Zhao 1999, pp. 260–261.

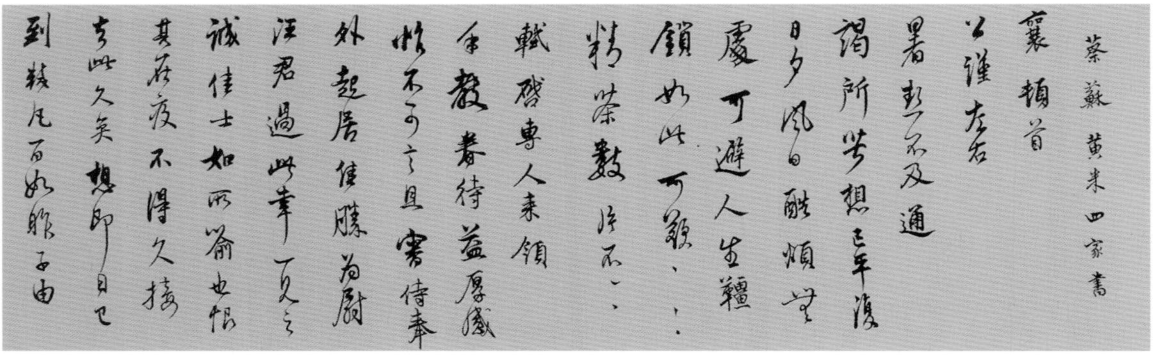

蔡蘇黃米四家書

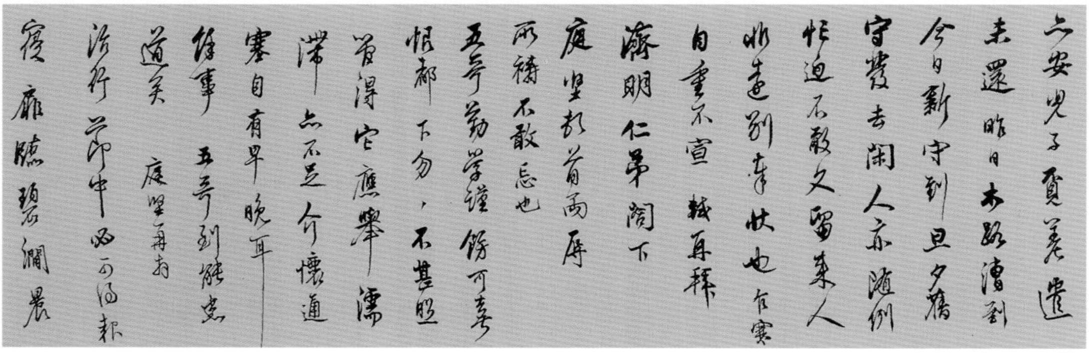

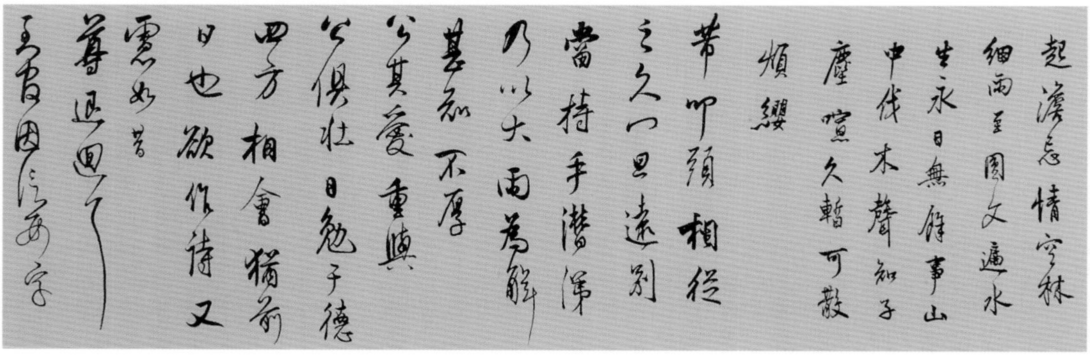

襄頓首

公謹左右

暑熱不及通

謁所苦想已平復

慶可避人生輕

日夕風日酷煩暑

鎖如此可厭

精茶數片不

載啟專人來領

手教春待益厚愧

帖不可言旦書侍奉

外起居佳勝為慰

誠佳士如兩箇也恨

汪君過此辈夏之

佳事五亭到縣烹

道矣

庭堅再拜

六安見子賢差遣

未還昨日夾路灘到

今日新守到旦夕搞

守費去閒人承隨例

作迫不敢久留柴人

非遠別李坦柴人

自雲不宣軾再拜

滌明仁果閣下

庭聖却首兩展

兩後不敢忘也

頓纓

起瀯忘情空林

細雨至園文通水

意命筆本為天

生永日無俗事山

中休木聲知子

色恼慢呈雲本

為散題家首特

帝叩頭相径

之久一旦遠別

當持手潛潸

乃以大雨為解

其怨不厚

公其愛重與

公俱壯日勉子德

四方相會猶有

日也欲作待又

雲如書

尊返迺了

因信函萅

古人書久横俱率

秋子久懷學一率

高義素沼多學真

回首宋人乃不爾如

吉有意學室室自也

蔡君謨書

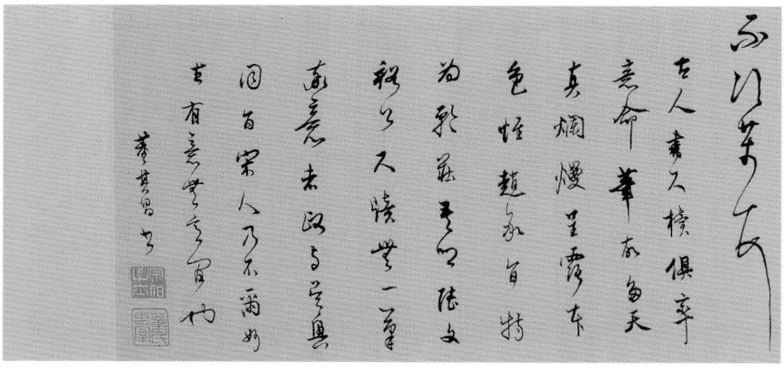

Chinese, Qing dynasty, 18th century
Silk *kesi* tapestry; dyed blue-black and undyed silk yarns in weft-faced
tabby-weave fabric utilizing the *kesi* tapestry technique to create calligraphy
H. 29.5 cm; L. 289.5 cm

Using a stark palette to simulate the appearance of ink on a silk ground, the weavers of this 115
textile have created a facsimile of a handscroll of cursive script calligraphy, complete with the
appearance of impressed seals of the artist at the far left. The red-seal paste vermilion of these
emblems is the only counterpoint to the black-and-white of the scroll. The weavers have thus
shown their skill all the more boldly, and the original patron must have marveled as do today's
viewers over their ability to capture the nuances of a fluid stroke of an ink-laden brush and to
go even further to convey the spirit of the personal calligraphic style of Ming scholar-official
Dong Qichang. In order to maximize their ability to create a natural flow of the curves of the
characters as well as to make a seamless length of silk for the handscroll, the weavers have
woven the scroll from end to end in one long segment.

This remarkable handscroll from the Qing palace reflects the Qianlong emperor's fascination
with calligraphic masterpieces by the the Four Song Masters, Cai Xiang (1012–1067), Su Shi
(1037–1101), Huang Tingjian (1045–1105) and Mi Fu (1052–1107), and by Ming dynasty
artist Dong Qichang (1555–1636).[1] Like the album of *Scenes of West Lake* (number 17), this
work reflects the Qianlong emperor's direct participation in the arts. The album presents
Qianlong's poetry, while this scroll presents one in a series of calligraphic works of art based on
the emperor's own artistic endeavor and on his study of works in the imperial collection. The
Qianlong emperor studied the works of the Four Song Masters and copied their works many
times throughout his long reign. The three installments of the imperial catalogs of painting and
calligraphy (*Shiqu Baoji*, published in 1744–5, 1793, and 1816) each record examples of
Qianlong's calligraphy using the Four Song Masters as models.[2] Qianlong also copied many of
Dong Qichang's renditions of works by these Four Masters of the Song. Calligraphy was in
many ways the most lofty of all the arts, with its attention to pure form paramount in both its
practice and its appreciation. To copy in this manner is called *lin*, a term that suggests an effort
to study and learn from a model while reproducing it. The emperor copied other models, but
works by the Four Song Masters and by Dong Qichang were his most frequent models, and their
works also formed an important core of calligraphic masterpieces in his imperial collection.

The weavers have captured every brushstroke of the original scroll written in ink on paper and
kept as part of the imperial art collections. In that work, Dong had copied four letters, one each
by the Four Song Masters. The specific model for this scroll must have been like two scrolls of
similar content now in the Beijing Palace Museum.[3] Tapestries (*kesi*) and embroideries were
listed in the imperial catalogs, suggesting that this woven handscroll of Dong Qichang's calligraphy

should not be viewed as a reproduction of a work of art but rather as a work of art in its own right. China had a long tradition of rendering religious texts into woven form,[4] always with a reverence for the process—the sustained effort and the painstaking technique added to the religious merit achieved by reproducing a text. In the present example, the pursuit of art as practiced by the Chinese scholar-artist supplied the motivation for this intense activity in weaving. This woven form of calligraphy preserves the fluidity of strokes originally made with the supple hair brush and in a sense commemorates the emperor's own frequent practice of applying brush-strokes of ink in the art of calligraphy.

[CB]

Calligraphy of the Four Masters [of the Northern Song Dynasty]: Cai [Xiang], Su [Shi], Huang [Tingjian], and Mi [Fu]

[Cai Xiang]
Xiang in deference;
Mr. Gongjin,
Because of the summer heat, I have not been able to write to request a visit. I assume that you have recovered from your illness. From day to night, wind and heat are bothersome. I have no place to hide. Alas, human life is bridled as such! Do you have some fine tea?

[Su Shi]
I have specially asked someone to come to pick it up. You personally instructed me and cared for me. I am mortified and speechless. I am consoled after hearing that you are cautious with official duties and you are living well.
Mr. Wang passed through, and I was fortunate to meet him. He is as fine a gentleman as you have informed me. I regret that he was in mourning, so I could not care for him long. He left here a while back, and should soon arrive. I am as usual. Ziyou is fine as well. My son went out to look for a job, and he has not returned yet.
Yesterday the imperial carriage passed through; today the new governor arrived. In a day the old governor left. Bureaucrats all follow the custom of feigning busyness; they dare not keep messengers waiting for long.
As I am not far away, you need not send letters.
The weather has suddenly become chilly. Please take care.
Su Shi, respectfully.

[Huang Tingjian]
Mr. Jiming, my young friend;
Tingjian in deference; I have two letters for you.
I dare not forget your greeting.
It is worthy of celebration that Wuqi studies hard and is cautious with his speech. I regret that I was in such a hurry in the capital that I could not take care of him. Even though he did not do well in the examination, there is nothing to worry about. Soon he will be a good scholar.
As for the rest of the matter, Wuqi will discuss it in detail after his arrival.
Tingjian in deference, again.
Zhixing will definitely be rewarded for his restraint and calm character.
With his bedroom facing a pure stream, he is able to forget human emotion when getting up in the morning. In an empty forest, fine rain falls, creating ripples all over the water. He has no other matters all day, but listens to the sound of woodcutting. I know he has been in the dusty world for long, and can temporarily toss away the troublesome official cap.

[Mi Fu]
Fu in deference;
I have followed you long, but soon I will depart to a faraway place.
I want to hold up my hand to weep, but I feel much more relieved if I cry

like heavy rain. I know I am not worthy, but you take good care of me. When
I was with you, you encouraged me to be virtuous. It was like old times
when we met in various places. I want to compose poetry, but I am afraid to
conjure up fond memories of the past. Therefore I retreat. After arriving
at my new post, I will write to report my safety.
Written by Fu.

[Dong Qichang]
The ancients had all practiced calligraphy for a long time, so when
writing letters, they all let the brush act on spontaneous inspiration. So
they are innocent and carefree, revealing their true natures. But only Zhao
Chengzhi (Mengfu) was especially formal, and the letters of Mr. Lu Wenyu of
our Ming dynasty are not carefree, matching the idea of Wuxing
(Zhao Mengfu). But Song-dynasty masters were different; the wonder of their
calligraphy is in its spontaneity.
[signed] Dong Qichang

[seals] *Zongbo xueshi; Dongshi Xuancai.*[5]

[translations by An-yi Pan]

Publications: Claudia Brown, "The Amy S. Clague Collection of Chinese Textiles,"
Orientations 31, no. 2 (February 2000), p. 42, fig. 14.

Technical analysis
Warp: Tan silk; Z twist; single ply. Count: 27 yarns per centimeter. The warps are running horizontally in the scroll.
Weft: Tan, dark blue and red silk; no apparent twist; no ply (bundled yarns not twisted together). Count: 27 yarns per
centimeter. *Weave: Kesi.* Tapestry is woven in the tapestry technique (weft faced tabby) with slit joins. There is eccentric weaving in the curves. The textile is adhered to paper (mounted as a handscroll) so only the obverse is available
for examination. *Dyeing*: Yarn dyed. *Selvages*: none remaining. All four edges are cut.

Scroll cover
Brocade.

Commentary
All decoration is woven, including the two seal impressions.

[MWG]

1   This scroll is virtually identical to another handscroll in the
    Liaoning Provincial Museum (see Yang et al. 1983, cat. no. 52).
    This is not surprising given the Qianlong emperor's admiration for
    Dong Qichang's calligraphy.

2   These figure very prominently among the imperial calligraphies
    recorded, with one example in the *Shiqu Baoji* (p. 285), and three
    each in the *Shiqu Baoji Xubian* (pp. 3131, 3132, 3473) and the
    Shiqu Baoji Sanbian (pp. 1305, 1306, and 1307).

3   For two handscrolls by Dong Qichang similar to the model for this
    handscroll, see Kansas City 1992, cat. nos. 10 (pp. 17-19 and
    203-204), and 64 (pp. 80-82 and 236-237). A handscroll by
    Dong Qichang after the calligraphy of the Four Song Masters
    is listed in the *Shiqu Baoji* (p. 539). According to the entry,
    the scroll was kept in Qianlong's study, the Yangxin Dian.

4   See for example, the tenth century Buddhist handscroll which
    presents in woven form a sutra of more than 5,000 characters.
    The work is preserved in the Liaoning Provincial Museum,
    Shenyang, and is described and illustrated by Zhao Feng 1999,
    cat. no. 10.07, pp. 314-319.

5   For comparative examples of these seals, see Celia Carrington Riely,
    in Kansas City 1992, p. 299.

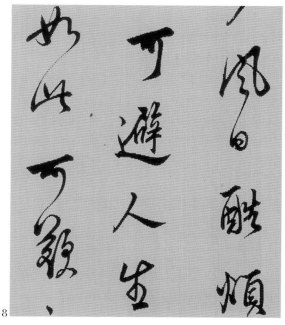

18

[Detail]

19 Silk-covered Box with Dragons among Clouds

Qing dynasty, 19th century
Silk *kesi* tapestry; dyed silk yarns of black, gray, and taupe in weft-faced
tabby-weave fabric utilizing the *kesi* tapestry technique to create
representational patterns
Front and back panels: H. 14 cm; W. 7.8 cm

The silk cover of this small container portrays—on back and front—a dragon exhaling a flaming pearl into a whirlpool, symbolizing his power to bring rain. Based on portrayals from as early as the Song dynasty (960–1279), the motif is rendered in shades of black, gray, and taupe to simulate the colors of ink brushwork in monochromatic painting. A tiny red flame designates the symbolic power of the jewel.

The tradition of portraying dragons in clouds—nearly always rendered in monochrome ink—is well represented in Song and Yuan dynasty paintings.[1] An early *kesi* rendition of the theme, probably a source for the Clague example, was woven to be mounted as a round fan. Dated to the Yuan dynasty, it is now in the collection of The Metropolitan Museum of Art.[2]

The Metropolitan Museum also possesses a set of five boxes with similar decoration, but with a red ground color,[3] dated to the late eighteenth to nineteenth century. The rectangular box of similar size within that set has been identified as a spectacle case. Perhaps the Clague example could have held eyeglasses, calling cards, or other items that had become increasingly popular to carry in the nineteenth century. Containers held on the belt by a cord, sometimes secured by a toggle, had been traditionally used to carry small items. This box may then show an adaptation of the tradition to modern fashion.

[CB]

Technical analysis
Warp: Tan silk; Z twist; no ply. Count: 32 yarns per centimeter. *Weft*: Polychrome silk; slight Z twist; 2–3 yarns treated as one but not twisted together. The yarns lie parallel to one another. Count: 32 yarns per centimeter. *Weave*: Kesi. The textile is woven in the tapestry technique (weft faced tabby) with slit joins. There is eccentric weaving in the curves. The weft has disappeared in several areas. *Dyeing*: Yarn dyed. *Selvages*: none.

Embellishments
All decoration is achieved through weaving. The black line outlining the dragon's nose was examined under high power optical microscope to see if it was a line of embroidery. It is not. The line is woven.

Commentary
This artifact is a five-sided box. The *kesi* textiles are the top and bottom of the box. The other three sides are covered with blue silk fabric. This box contains a second five-sided box. The top and bottom of the inner box is white silk satin fabric and the three remaining sides are covered with blue silk satin fabric. The silk satin fabric is a 5/1 weave. The inner structure of both boxes is a thick paper. A new blue silk tassel was added in 1997. The textile was examined under an optical microscope at Arizona State University's Center for Solid State Science on 28 October 1998.

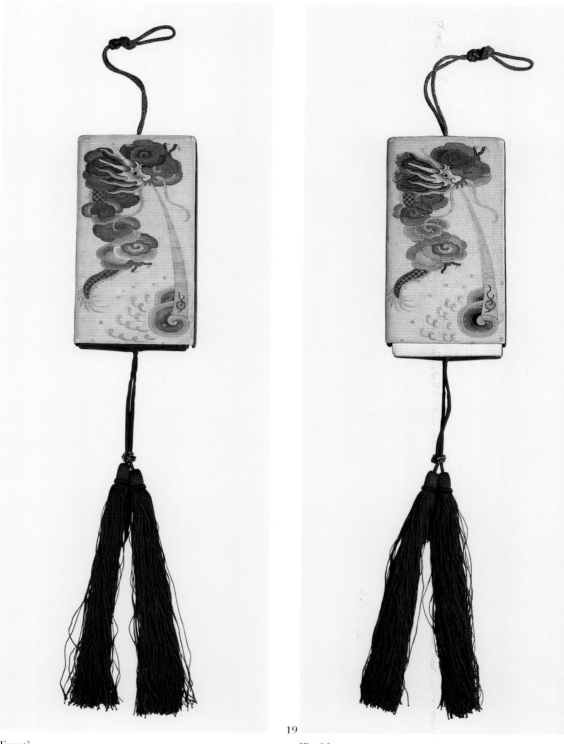

19

[Front]

19

[Back]

Photographs were taken of the ground fabric weave pattern and the weave of the dragon's flame. A kesi fan with a similar motif in the collection of The Metropolitan Museum of Art, New York (accession number 47.18.42, see New York 1997, cat. no. 27) has a weave of wefts passing over two warps for the portion of fabric representing the dragon's breath. This is not the case here.

[MWG]

1   One of the best known of these is the handscroll by Chen Rong, dated 1244, painted in ink with touches of red. The scroll was formerly in the Qing imperial collection, and is now in the Museum of Fine Arts, Boston, accession number 17.1697; the scroll is published in Boston 1997, pp. 197–200, cat. no. 92.

2   Accession number 47.18.42; illustrated and described in New York 1997, cat. no. 27. The authors link the fan to Yuan dynasty texts describing fans for use in the Duanwu festival.

3   See Milhaupt 1992, fig. 9.

Numbers 20–28   Embroideries

122

20

20

[Detail]

Ming Dynasty, 15th century
   Silk of broken twill weave, embroidered with polychrome silk threads using
   laid and couched, split, satin, and outline stitches
Five sections:
H. 16.5 cm, W. 12.5–13 cm; Band: W. 3 cm; L. 46 cm;
Leather tie: W. 1.5 cm, L. 27 cm

This Buddhist ritual diadem (Tibetan, *rig-na*) of the type used in Tantric practices dates from 123 the fifteenth century, a period when China had close religious and cultural ties with Tibet. The diadem is composed of five sections joined at the lower edge by a band with leather ties on either end. Each of the five panels displays an enthroned figure, one of the Five Tathagatas (Transcendent or Dhyani Buddhas, also known as the Five Jinas): from left to right, they are Ratnasambhava (yellow), Akshobhya (blue), Vairochana (white), Amitabha (red), and Amoghasiddhi (green). Each Buddha sits in the lotus position on a lotus throne adorned with drapery that indicates the symbol of that particular Buddha. Each throne is flanked by a pair of white elephants, a pair of dark blue lions, and a pair of light blue rams. Centered above each Buddha is a *garuda*, a protective mythical bird, flanked by a pair of green dragons from whose mouths a flaming pearl issues forth. These images are enclosed by an overall border of dark blue ornamented by gold dots representing jewels. Outside this border are delicately shaded cloud scrolls in blue, green, gold, and white. This pattern is in turn enclosed by a border of multi-color lines. At the top of each section is a Sanskrit character, enclosed in a roundel, that identifies each Buddha. The five sections of the crown are edged with a narrow cord that also connects them together. The headband at the bottom depicts repeated gold *vajras*, or thunderbolts, interspersed with decorative motifs against a dark blue background bordered in gold.

Considered to have overcome the cycle of rebirth and suffering through attainment of spiritual knowledge, the Five Jinas represent the five directions, the five wisdoms, the five senses, the five elements, the five colors, the five addictions, and the five Buddha clans.[1] The Five Jina diadem was worn by monks, oracles, and lay healers for ritual and ceremonial purposes, including initiations, exorcisms, and funerals.[2] Upon donning the diadem, the monk becomes homologized with the divine essence and a receptacle for cosmic forces. Photographs taken in Tibet as late as 1928 document this widespread usage.[3]

Two similar diadems belonging to the Hall Collection Trust were exhibited at the Hong Kong Museum of Art.[4] Both depict the Five Jinas with similar iconography, although one is embroidered (dated seventeenth century) while the other is brocade (dated fifteenth century). The embroidered one is also accented with borders of seed pearls. Neither example has the lovely embroidered headband of the Clague example. Two other similar examples were illustrated in a recent sale catalog.[5] One is embroidered and the other is brocade, and the iconography is virtually identical to the Clague example, although both are later in date. The Los Angeles County Museum of Art has a diadem also dated to the fifteenth century, executed in needleloop embroidery.[6]

In the Newark Museum is an embroidered crown (fifteenth century) with markedly different pictorial treatment of the Five Jinas, including stylized lotus flower thrones and an elimination of the decorative motifs that imitate jewels or beading.[7] The Metropolitan Museum of Art in New York has a painted diadem (late fourteenth-early fifteenth century) on which the seated Buddha figures are given more elaborate drapery and Nepalese-style crowns, although the decorative and animal motifs appear similar to the Clague example.[8] The above similarities to the Clague diadem suggest a date in the fifteenth century, confirmed by radiocarbon dated performed at The University of Arizona.[9]

[JB]

Publications: Claudia Brown, "The Amy S. Clague Collection of Chinese Textiles," *Orientations* 31, no. 2 (February 2000), p. 37, fig. 8.

Technical analysis
Ground
There are two different fabrics on the obverse side of this textile but, except for color, they have the same characteristics so the following information covers both. The five main sections have tan color fabric while the band has dark blue fabric. *Warp*: tan and dark blue silk; slight Z twist; single ply. Count: 36 yarns per centimeter. The warp runs horizontally in the five main sections, vertically in the band fabric. *Weft*: Gold and dark blue silk; no apparent twist; single ply. Count: 30 yarns per centimeter. *Weave*: 3/1 broken twill. Condition: Voids at some corners and edges. Interior is in good condition. *Dyeing*: Yarn dyed. *Selvages*: none.

Embroidery
Threads: Polychrome silk, bundle of filaments without apparent twist. Thread outlining motifs: bundle of white silk filaments wrapped (Z twist) with gold adhered to paper. All are attached with laid and couched stitch. Cord outlining the five sections: Cabled, Z twist, two ply, green silk yarns with no apparent twist. *Stitches*: laid and couched, split, satin, outline.

Band
Additional type of silk decorative thread. There are six rows at top and six rows at bottom, colored yellow tan, light blue, green. The type of twist alternates with the rows. Rows 1,3,5 have Z twist while rows 2,4,6 have S twist. When placed next to each other it appears there are three rows of a braided thread.

Lining
The lining of the five top sections is a yellow silk brocade fabric. Warp: 52 yarns per centimeter. Weft: 30 yarns per centimeter. An inscription in red ink appears on the lining of the center panel. Wax spots dot the surface. Other: There is a white material interlining the five main sections (visible through the voids of the lining) which imparts stiffness to the panels. It consists of three layers with the outer two composed of a woven fabric, and the inner a tabby of very open mesh weave perhaps only 4 yarns per centimeter.

Commentary: The green silk lining of the band is probably brocade although the caked on skin oils greatly obscure the woven motif.

[MWG]

1   Frederic 1995, pp. 125–147 gives a thorough treatment of the Five Jinas.

2   Gluckman 2000, pp. 92–95.

3   Aris 1992, pp. 88, 92, 115, 116 and 117.

4   Hong Kong 1995, pp. 190–193.

5   Spink & Son 1994, p. 47.

6   Gluckman 2000, p. 92.

7   Barrett 1998, p. 21.

8   Kossak 1998, p. 62.

9   Sample date number: AA-4260. According to Timothy Jull on the basis of the radiocarbon tests, this textile can be assigned to the period 1413–1442 with sixty eight per cent confidence or to the period 1330–1484 with ninety five per cent confidence. Letter dated 27 January 1998 from A.J.T. Jull, The University of Arizona NSF - Arizona AMS Facility, Tucson, to Arthur Leeper, then owner of the textile.

Ming dynasty, probably 1400–1435
    Silk gauze with needleloop embroidery; navy blue ribbed gauze ground
    with detached loop embroidery in polychrome silk yarns over backing
    paper with gold over a ground of bole
H. 13 cm; W. 56.5 cm (max)

This silk fragment is embroidered in needleloop technique with a pattern of five lotus blossoms, [125] each divided into nine stylized petals. The ground fabric (see micrographic detail p. 129) itself is extraordinary: a dark blue, finely ribbed gauze, a luxurious cloth[1] regardless of its additional embellishment. The embellishing embroidery, splendid indeed, displays a great variety of colored silk threads—including dark blue, light blue, dark green, light green, yellow, and white—worked with precision in a variety of detached, "needlelooped" stitches[2] over a gold surfaced paper. The gold of the backing paper is applied over a pink bole (see micrographic detail; for an explanation of bole, see number 2). Each blossom is different; there are no exactly repeating patterns, but there is a continuous rhythm and proportion. The centers of each blossom are accented with embroiderer's knots. The lower border is a slightly smaller rendition of the top one. No selvages remain to indicate the size of the original woven ground; the surviving fragments differ in width but have a consistent height.

The stately pacing of the motifs suggests a link to palace designs of the early fifteenth century.[3] This proposed dating is supported by a radiocarbon test performed on a sample removed from a nearly identical fragment.[4] A striking resemblance to cloisonné vessels of the early fifteenth century has been noted by scholars,[5] and comparable examples[6] are associated with the Xuande reign (1426–1435). Also similar in decoration are Yongle period wooden sutra covers of red lacquer and engraved gold (qiangjin).[7] These examples have Buddhist symbols on lotus pedestals within the scrolling vines rather than lotus blossoms, but the rhythmically scrolling vines have a close resemblance to these needleloop examples. Another embroidered fragment, attributed to the fourteenth century, combines a scrolling vine with peony, lotus, and three jewels.[8] This similarity, together with the shape of the surviving fragments, suggest that these cloths might have been used to adorn covers for Tibetan-style Buddhist texts.

The resemblance to cloisonné goes beyond the similar motifs. The stitches of the scrolling vines, the border patterns and portions of the blossoms surround the gold backing paper in a way that seems parallel to the cells of enamels formed of wires enhanced by gilding. Also the mixing of colors in certain parts of the flowers forms an effect similar to the "mixed colors" of Ming dynasty enamelers. The effect of combining bright primary colors with areas of gold is parallel; the needlework adds however the further dimension of the pattern and texture of the individual stitches. Precedents for both the cloisonné and the needlelooped versions of the pattern may ultimately be found in jewelry, particularly where bright-colored semi-precious stones would have been surrounded by gold, and often gold-granulation work.[9] Certainly the combination of gold and bright colors in each of these artforms creates a gem-like effect.

126

21

21

[Detail: front]

127

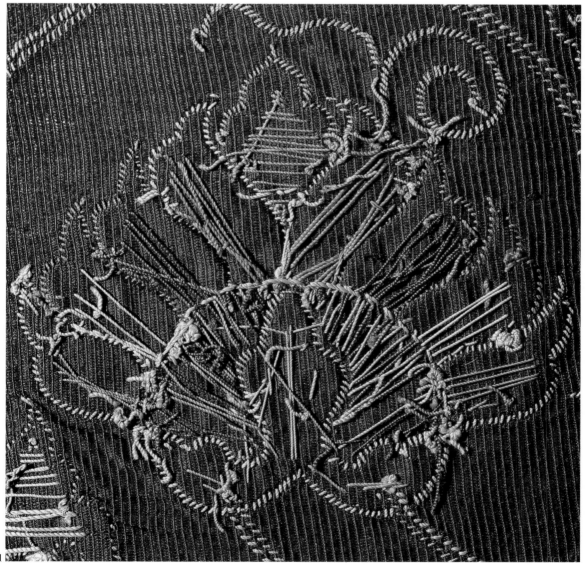

21

[Detail: back]

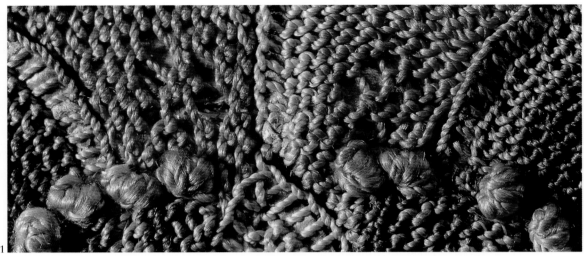

21
[Detail]

128 Surviving from the fourteenth-fifteenth centuries are a number of important Chinese textiles of lamaist Buddhist subjects. One group, a number of votive panels in dark blue silk embroidered with gold-wrapped and polychrome silk threads in museums and private collections,[10] has been discussed by several authors and attributed to the Yuan dynasty, but recently was convincingly dated to the Yongle (1403–1424) era.[11] The border patterns are very similar in appearance to those in the present textile, although in the needlelooped example a ladder stitch shows gold-surfaced paper behind whereas in the embroideries a gold-wrapped laid-and-couched thread is used. Based on the strong affinities between these works, and confirmed by the radiocarbon evidence cited above, a date within the first decades of the fifteenth century is proposed.

[CB]

Publications: Claudia Brown, "The Amy S. Clague Collection of Chinese Textiles," *Orientations* 31, no. 2 (February 2000), p.38, figs. 9 and 9a.

Technical analysis
Ground
Warp: Dark blue silk; Z twist; 2-ply, Z. Count: 68 yarns per centimeter. Other: Warps run horizontal in this piece. *Weft*: Foundation: Dark blue silk; no apparent twist; single ply. Count: 9 bundles per centimeter. Numerous filaments are found in a bundle. *Weave*: Simple gauze with a unit of two warps. In this weave, the warp yarns are manipulated rather than the weft yarns. *Dyeing*: Yarn dyed. *Selvages*: none remaining.

Embroidery
Thread: yellow in color, heavy, prominent Z twist, 2-ply. Other: A gilded paper lies under all of the embroidery. The gold leaf is attached to a gray paper substrate over pink bole. *Stitches*: Detached looping, open chain, knots.

Commentary
Embroidery threads begin stitching with a knot and end with a knot. The textile was examined under high magnification with an optical microscope at Arizona State University's Center for Solid State Science, 28 October 1998. There is a photo of the weave of the textile and a photo of the gilded paper.

[MWG]

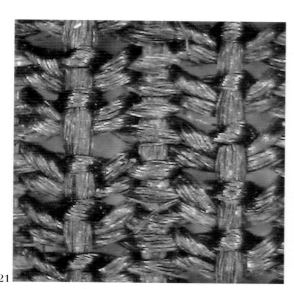

21

[Detail: optical microscopy—weave of the textile]

21

[Detail: optical microscopy—the gilded paper]

1   For a description of ribbed gauze weaves, see Zhao 1999,
    pp. 235-236.

2   On the needleloop technique, see Berger 1989, Sonday and
    Maitland 1989, New York 1997 (pp. 165-166), and Zhao 2000.

3   The scrolling lotus blossoms here are perhaps closer to the early
    15th century style (for example, see Rawson 1984, fig. 66)
    than to examples from the Xuande period (1426-1435; for an
    example, see Valenstein 1989, fig. 150).

4   The fragment tested, sample date Arizona AA-4477, is illustrated
    and described in Spink 1989 b, pp. 20 and 161, no. 11. The results
    are said to support a dating to the period 1326-1416 with sixty eight
    per cent confidence or the period 1300-1430 with ninety five
    per cent confidence. The same piece was also published in Sonday
    and Maitland 1989, p. 60, fig. 4. Although the Spink example is
    listed as possibly having gilded animal skin, analysis of the Clague
    piece suggested paper as the likely substrate for the gold leaf under
    the blossoms, in the vines, and in the border pattern. Another
    similar fragment is illustrated by Simcox 1989, p. 25, fig. 9.

5   Spink 1989 b, p. 20.

6   See New York 1989, cat. nos. 9, 13 and 15, examples dated to the
    first half of the 15th century.

7   See one example in Gluckman 2000, p. 95, fig. 6; and other
    illustrated in Berger and Bartholomew, 1995, p. 188, fig. 1,
    dated 1410.

8   Sale catalog, *Textile Art from the Silk Road*, The Textile Gallery,
    February 1998.

9   See, for example, White and Bunker, 1994, cat. nos. 70 and 86. I am
    grateful to Robert Mowry who pointed out this similarity to me.

10 In this group are several small votive panels on a dark blue silk
    ground, recently emerging from Tibet and now in various collections.
    In private collections, including one panel in the Hall Collection
    Trust, is a series published in Hong Kong 1995, cat. nos. 22a-h.
    The Los Angeles County Museum of Art acquired one example;
    accession number M.88.121, illustrated in Gluckman 2000, fig. 5
    and 5a. Cleveland Museum of Art also has a panel; accession
    number 1991.2. For an illustration of the Cleveland example and a
    discussion and diagram of how the panels would have been hung,
    see New York 1997, cat. no. 63, especially p. 209.

11 Reynolds 1995 a, pp. 50-57, and Gluckman 2000, pp. 95-97.
    For a discussion of textiles relating to the Yongle emperor's
    patronage of Buddhism, see New York 1997, p. 166.

22 Rectangular Silk Altar, Table, or Desk Frontal with Pleated Valance and with Decoration of Dragons and Flaming Pearls amid Clouds and Waves

Ming to Qing dynasty, 17–18th century
  Silk gauze with counted stitch embroidery in polycrome silk threads;
  minor ink details
H. 79 cm; W. 256.5 cm

22

This densely embroidered cloth is designed with three large five-clawed dragons. Its width is generous enough to wrap around three sides of a large table or desk. The dragons are positioned so that the main one would show on the front of the table, while the two smaller ones would be displayed on the sides. The pleats of the valance were probably intended to be distributed with three on each side and five on the front, and displayed in that manner would have a symmetrical alternation of blue and white dragons.

The central dragon, slightly larger than the others, clasps a flaming pearl. The two smaller flanking dragons grasp colorful clouds in their forward claws. All three dragons rise up above a lively pattern of waves cascading against colorful rocks which seem to jut out of the water like precious gemstones. Surrounding the dragons are variegated clouds. All of these motifs may be seen in the costumes of the Qing dynasty court and all refer to the cosmos and the power of the emperor. The dragons in roundels on the valance offer a slightly different imagery, one which may relate to the archaic dragons to be found in ancient jades and bronze mirrors in the imperial collection of antiquities. This archaistic dragon, sometimes described as immature, is often termed a *zhilong*. The roundels with their sinuously curving interior motifs stand out against a background of rectilinear keyfret patterns.

A close look at the stitches reveals a painstaking technique in which a loosely woven gauze is embroidered with a stitch approximately 2 millimeters in length, each covering two woven units. Called counted stitch (*nazhen*), this technique produces a thick and heavy fabric. In this textile, the embroiderer has covered the entire gauze ground; thus it may be considered *najin* (full count embroidery).[1] The surface of the gauze is entirely stitched in silk yarns of various colors, including shades of red, blue, green, brown, gray, and black.[2] The grayish brown (taupe) threads have deteriorated, revealing the yellowish gold colored gauze underneath. Some accents have been brushed on in ink after the embroidery was finished. These can be seen in the dragons' horns, eyes, teeth, and claws, and on the barbs of their tails. Faint blue lines were added in the frothing waves. These accents were inadvertently omitted in the dragon's claw at the far right of the textile; examining this area, one can see readily how the ink details functioned subtly but essentially to complete the illusion.

The construction of the frontal fabric and valance and their linings may be original. The slightly larger gauge of the stitches in the area covered by the valance (see technical analysis below) suggests that that portion was not meant to be seen by the original makers of the textile. This assertion is further borne out by the signs of wear on the lining.

Enclosing a table by wrapping cloth about its legs was a well established practice by Ming times. Woodblock prints of Ming date show tables draped on three sides both in domestic interiors and in temple settings, and often seem to be used for covering a magistrate's desk.[3] The counted-stitch embroidery may have provided a desirable type of textile for such uses; its heavy and consistent fabric would have hung evenly and resisted drafts.[4]

The present example, with its rampant, five-clawed dragons, was probably commissioned for the Qing palace as these motifs were appropriate for the emperor and princes and their consorts. As on court garments, the five-clawed dragon (*long*) is associated specifically with the emperor and his inner family. The mountains rising from waves, denoting qualities of longevity and abundance, also parallel Qing court garments. Distinctive in this context is the appearance of the dragon clutching the pearl rather than pursuing it (on the symbolism of the dragon and the jewel, see number 2). This links the altar frontal to a number of works from the Kangxi era in which striking examples of this motif occur.[5] These similarities support an attribution to the early Qing court, probably the reign of Kangxi (1662–1722).

132

[CB]

Publications: Claudia Brown, "The Amy S. Clague Collection of Chinese Textiles," *Orientations* 31, no. 2 (February 2000), p. 38, fig. 10.

Technical analysis
Ground
Warp: Gold colored silk; Z twist; single ply. Count: 22 yarns per centimeter. Warp yarns are in pairs so there are 11 pairs of warp yarns per centimeter. Warps run horizontal in this piece. *Weft*: Gold colored silk; no apparent twist; single ply. Count: 11 yarns per centimeter. *Weave*: Simple gauze with a unit of two warps which makes an open weave. (In a gauze weave the binding is achieved when warp yarns are twisted after a weft is inserted.) *Dyeing*: Yarn dyed. *Selvages*: none.

Embellishments
The entire surface of the ground fabric is covered with stitching.

Embroidery
Polychrome silk; no apparent twist; single ply. Stitches: Brick stitch. There are five stitches per centimeter. The majority of the stitches pass over two pairs of warp yarns. The area under the valance looks as if it is covered with another stitch but the difference is that the embroidery thread passes over three pairs of warp yarns instead of just two.
Other added items: The top of the textile has a band of silk satin fabric, dark blue in color, that extends across the entire width of the textile. Both the main body and the pleated valance are stitched to this band.

Lining
There are two different linings. The fabric under the valance is a gold colored silk damask. The fabric lining the textile is a gold colored silk satin.

Commentary
A tabby pattern shows through the voids of the embroidery. It is the reverse side of the satin weave lining, not an additional fabric.

[MWG]

---

1 Described by Zhao 1999, p. 345. This type of embroidery has also been termed "woven in" embroidery or "woven gauze," see Gao 1987, p. 33.

2 The black appears to be a very dark brown.

3 See Rongbaozhai 1958, plates 110 and 111. Clunas 1992 (p. 67) discusses his observations on the draping of three sides of officials' tables.

4 For an illustration of a Qing dynasty counted-stitch table frontal draped on a table, see Kerr 1991, p. 114, pl. 44. The authors point out that the even tension of the embroidery makes the frontal hang smoothly.

5 See for example, Yang Xin 1988, figs. 127 and 129.

23 Rectangular Silk Panel with Celestial Palace Rising above Waves, probably a portion of a Daoist robe

Qing dynasty, 18th century
  Gold-colored silk four-end satin with embroidery in laid and couched gold-wrapped
    threads and in polychrome silk threads over paper faced with gold leaf
  H. 63.5 cm; W. 59.5 cm

This rectangular silk satin panel originally formed the central back panel of a robe for a Daoist priest. The deep gold-colored satin is embroidered so densely that the ground fabric shows only as a background to the laid and couched wave pattern in gold wrapped threads. Much of the surface was originally embellished with gilt paper which would have been seen through looped embroidery stitches and ladder chain stitches.[1] Traces of the gilt paper remain in the large circle motif and the curling shapes which embellish it, in the motifs to either side of the celestial palace and the half circle surrounding the rays that emanate from it, in the foundation of the palace and in the rays themselves, and in the circles around the sun and moon. Within the central roundel are thirty-five circles of gold wrapped threads laid and couched in a tight concentric pattern. Outside the roundel, there are twenty-two larger circles together with two smaller ones. The main motif is a multi-storied tower on a block foundation rising upon a stylized rock or mountain. The mountain is described by truncated and scalloped vertical layers which are pointed below and flattened above to form a platform for the building. Emanating from each story of the tower are rays of light described by alternating bands of shades of blue and gold colored embroidery threads. Flying cranes flank the sides of the tower. Below the main roundel, long tailed phoenixes descend. Above it are the sun (upper left) and the moon (upper right). Each has its legendary symbols, the crow and the rabbit, respectively.

Three garments of similar technique and with very similar scenes have been illustrated in recent publications.[2] One of these, a robe in The Minneapolis Institute of Arts, bears an inscription dated to the eleventh year of the Qianlong reign (1746). In each of these examples the celestial palace and related motifs are depicted as here with gold wrapped, laid and couched threads, and strips of gilt paper. The group has recently been discussed[3] in relation to the needlelooping technique which had flourished in Yuan and Ming times but has generally been regarded as rare in the Qing. This group of three garments, and this fragment in the Clague collection, are so similar in workmanship and detail that they were probably made in the same workshop. Each employs a technique in which virtually all of the threads remain on the front of the garment. A fourth garment, now in the Victoria and Albert Museum[4] is attributed to the nineteenth century. Its bolder colors and sparser motifs seem to set it apart from the eighteenth century examples, and its wave patterns of couched gold wrapped threads run vertically rather than horizonatally

Daoist robes are generally simple in construction and rich in decoration. This fragment probably came from a garment without tailoring or sleeves, a type sometimes called a *jiangyi* or robe of descent, a term which evokes the meditative transcendence of the priest who wears it.[5]

134

23

23

[Detail]

The main motifs form a cosmological diagram, the Daoist heavenly palace appearing among waves and clouds while above the sun and moon complete the imagery. The formula is at least as old as the Han dynasty and may be seen in an early form in the now famous banner excavated from tomb number 1 at Mawangdui, Changsha, Hunan.[6] Its use in a specifically Daoist context to illustrate the Isles of the Immortals (Penglai) in the form of an icon is documented in wall paintings of the fourteenth century, notably in wall paintings at the Yonglegong in Shansi province and others preserved in the Royal Ontario Museum.[7] Banners carried by the devotees pictured in these murals represent a low palace building rising on a rock in turn rising from the sea. The roof of the building emanates rays of light. The sun and moon disks float to either side. This imagery evolved into the more complex motif seen commonly in the Daoist robes of the Qing period, usually described as representing a five-story pagoda, the *san qing* (three pure) abodes of primary deities in the Daoist pantheon, and the heavens, including the sun, moon and constellations.[8] The stars are symbolized in the large circles of couched gold-wrapped threads both within and just outside the circle which surrounds the heavenly palace. The sun and moon, are raised above and between them are three additional roundels, signifying the three "Pure Ones"; in some examples these each enclose a small tower or building, but here employ the abstract symbol of the *ruyi* against a background of multicolored bands which appear to emanate from the celestial palace itself. Flying cranes add their own auspicious symbolism of long life and transcendence.

[CB]

Technical analysis
Warp: Gold colored silk; Z twist; 2-ply, S. Count: 30 yarns per centimeter. *Weft*: Gold colored silk; slight Z twist; single ply. Count: 54 yarns per centimeter. *Weave*: 4 end satin. Some photo-chemical damage. *Dyeing*: Yarn dyed. *Selvages*: none.

Embroidery
Threads: 1) Light green, green, blue, dark blue, yellow heavy silk yarn; Z twist; 2-ply, S. Location: The birds, and other design motifs. 2) Bundle of yellow silk fibers wrapped with gold adhered to substrate; no apparent twist to silk fibers, gold wrapped Z twist. Location: All circles, outline of decorative motifs, cross hatch background pattern. Condition: Worn on surface. Much gold is missing. *Stitches*: Stab stitch, laid and couched stitch.
Other added items: A gilded paper lies under the outline of the bird's wings, under the bird's eye and the ring around the center medallion. It has a layer of bole, a shell pink color, under the gilding.

[MWG]

1   These are similar in character to those diagramed in Sonday and Maitland 1989, diagram 3, although the threads here are tightly twisted. The authors are grateful to Milton Sonday for examining photographs of this textile and offering insights into its technique (personal communications to Amy S. Clague, dated 11 December 1997 and 4 August 1998).

2   New York 1931, page 79, fig. 38, illustrates a similar section of a garment in The Metropolitan Museum of Art (MMA 35.84.1). The back of a similar garment in The Minneapolis Institute of Arts, inscribed with a date equivalent to 1746, is published in New York 1945, plate 47. The third, in a private collection in Paris, is illustrated by Zhao 2000, p. 52, figs. 15 and 15a. Yet another similar example was partially illustrated in New York 1931, figs. 37 and 38. The Paris example is extremely close to the Clague example, except that its satin ground is dark blue in color. This creates a contrasting effect quite different from the gold-on-gold appearance of the Clague piece.

3   Zhao 2000, pp. 51-52; Zhao considers these a Qing variant of needlelooping.

4   Published by Wilson 1995, p. 42, fig. 1, and p. 49, fig. 10. A somewhat similar Daoist priest's robe is in The Art Institute of Chicago, published in Chicago 1964, n. p.

5   Wilson 1995, p. 43.

6   Zhao 1999, p. 297, fig. 10.00d.

7   For an illustration of the Toronto murals, dated by inscription to 1371, see Brown, "Chinese Scholars' Rocks and the Land of Immortals: Some Insights from Painting," fig. 4, in Cambridge 1997, p. 67. For the Yonglegong murals, dated by inscription to 1362, see Jin 1988, cat. nos. 88-89.

8   Hong Kong 1995, p. 186, cat. no. 48.

136

24

Shaped Silk Panel with Roundel of Garden Rock, Magnolia,
and Peonies within Borders of Peaches, Bats, and
Other Auspicious Symbols

Qing dynasty, 18th to early 19th century
Embroidered silk; yellow ground in four-end satin weave embroidered in
polychrome silk threads and couched with bundled silk threads wrapped with
paper strips faced with gold
H. 79 cm; W. 73.5 cm

This satin panel with seven-lobed top is embroidered with three zones of decoration. Along its outer edge are twenty parallel gold-wrapped threads laid and couched in pairs to follow the perimeter, and within that a border of ten parallel couched gold-wrapped threads repeats the shape of the exterior, including the seven lobes at the top. Between these two golden borders a symmetrically organized series of stylized lotus blossoms is linked by scrolling patterns of leaves and stems and interspersed with flying bats. The stylized flowers have seeds suggested by knotted gold wrapped threads. Within the inner border is a pattern of peaches in a continuous fruiting vine. Among the peaches are flying bats. These animals are portrayed in varying poses, organized into a bilaterally symmetrical composition, and satin-stitched in shades of red, pink, and white, and outlined by gold-wrapped threads. The peach leaves and stems are embroidered in satin stitch in shades of green. The third and central zone of decoration is a roundel depicting a scene of a garden rock, a flowering peony, and a magnolia intertwined. The garden rock is embroidered in shades of blue and green. Ink outlines showing within the holes of the rock may have been guidelines for the embroiderer, but since they do not appear elsewhere in the composition they are more likely added as accents. The peony blossoms are rendered with an illusion of three dimensions, their leaves embroidered with shades of yellow, green, and blue and outlined with gold wrapped threads. The magnolia tree is described by silvery gray threads in satin stitch for the trunk and white for its distinctive blossoms. Two crested, long tailed white birds nestle in its branches just to the left of center. Atop the scene is a pair of fish and a pair of *ruyi* scepters—paired motifs perhaps intended as auspicious wishes for conjugal happiness—positioned as if suspended under a musical stone, the texture of the latter suggested by tiny knots. Above is a ribboned and flame emitting jewel. At the very pinnacle of the composition is depicted a vase in the "double gourd" shape decorated with stylized bats. Surrounding the vase are flowering and fruiting gourd vines.

The scene of the central roundel recalls the composition of *penjing* (*bonsai*) arrangements. The forms within the roundel are carefully shaded by the embroiderer to suggest three dimensional qualities and the motifs are positioned as a representational scene rather than a decorative pattern. The shading and pictorialism suggest a link to eighteenth century enamels associated with the Qing court, especially painted enamels with a yellow ground, such as flourished in the Yongzheng (1723–1735) and Qianlong (1736–1795) eras. The concept of positioning a pictorial scene within a decorative border relates closely to the style that can be seen in painted enamels on metal,[1] and also in cloisonné enamels, for example, a *bianhu* (flask) with roundel of magnolia, peony, crab apple, and garden rock in the Phoenix Art Museum.[2] Sometimes these

[Detail]

roundels position auspicious symbols in a pictorial scene to form a rebus. Terese Bartholomew[3] has identified this particular combination, the tree peony (*mudan*, also called *fuguihua* or "flower of wealth and rank") with white magnolia (*yulan*) and crab apple (*haitang*), as forming the auspicious phrase *yutang fugui*, meaning "wealth and rank in the jade hall," a reference to success in the Hanlin Academy, the highest honor in the civil service. Bartholomew[4] has identified additional rebuses in the present textile, including the pair of birds, *shoudai niao* (birds with longevity ribbons) or Paradise Flycatchers, symbolizing longevity. She further explains that the:

> bats and peaches stand for *fushou shuangquan*, "may both blessings and longevity be complete." The motif of gourd vines spilling out of a double gourd surmounting the piece stands for *zisun wandai*, "ten thousand generations of sons and grandsons." The lithophone (*qing*) and the double fish stand for *jiqing youyu*, "may there be an abundance of joy and happiness."

Such complex iconography links this textiles with jades and other decorative arts of the nineteenth century.[5]

Probably embroidered to serve as a cushion cover for a throne, this satin panel with its lobed shape would have been joined to additional matching fabric pieces.[6] The bright yellow color of the satin ground suggests that the cushion cover was made for use in the imperial palace, where the color yellow was associated with the emperor, princes of high rank, and imperial consorts of high rank. The use of yellow-ground textiles as palace furnishings is documented in a number of examples, including a large *kesi* floor covering in the Royal Ontario Museum.[7] Yellow-ground silk panels once used for upholstering cushions are well known in western collections, some brocaded with medallions of dragons,[8] and others embroidered on satin with floral and other auspicious motifs.[9] The palace collection in Beijing retains many examples as well.[10] A full set of cushions might include a seat cushion, a back cushion, and two elbow rests.[11]

Throne cushions shown in formal imperial portraits record the use of bats and peaches together with the patterns of precious objects and waves that were standard for court robes.[12] Roundels with dragons adorned the cushions upon which emperors sat.[13] In these formal portraits there is no suggestion of a back cushion for the throne. Back cushions do appear in slightly less formal settings, for example, in informal portraits where the emperor is shown engaging in calligraphy.[14] Cushions of this shape are currently displayed in the Yangxindian, for example, a hall in the palace used for "nourishing the spirit" with literary pursuits.[15] The imagery on this particular cushion cover, with its allusions to conjugal harmony, suggest it may have been used in the quarters of imperial consorts.

[CB]

Publications: Claudia Brown, "The Amy S. Clague Collection of Chinese Textiles," *Orientations* 31, no. 2 (February 2000), p. 43, fig. 15.

Technical analysis

Warp: yellow silk; slight Z twist; undetermined ply. Count: 30 yarns per centimeter. Other: Warps run horizontal in this textile. *Weft*: Foundation: Yellow silk; no apparent twist; single ply. Count: 51 yarns per centimeter. Wefts run vertical in this textile. *Weave*: 4 end satin. Condition: A paste-like substance (an adhesive from a label?) adheres to surface of embroidery threads at top, proper right side. *Dyeing*: Yarn dyed. *Selvages*: none visible.

Embroidery

Threads: Primary: polychrome silk; no apparent twist; single ply. Core yarns: pale orange silk; no twist; no ply (bundled yarns not twisted together). Wrapping: gold leaf adhered to paper; Z twist. There is a layer of a pink substance between gold and paper. Another gold thread with different characteristics is found in the rows of laid and couched gold threads around the perimeter of the textile. Core yarns: yellow silk; tight Z twist; 3-ply. Wrapping: Gold leaf adhered to paper, Z twist. There is a layer of a pink substance between the gold and the paper. *Stitches*: satin, French knots, outline, laid and couched.

Other added items

There is a line of very short sewing machine stitches around the perimeter of the textile. There is a second line of machine stitches around the top edge that also catches the lining.

Lining

Weft pattern weave silk fabric, faded yellow in color. Probably not original. There are several other pieces of fabric attached to the textile between the textile and the lining in the bottom proper left corner, perhaps including a portion of the original lining.

[MWG]

1   See for example, Hong Kong 1987, cat. no. 45, a fish bowl with scrolling flowers against a yellow ground, surrounding a pictorial scene.

2   Gift of Robert H. Clague, accession number 1982.216, see Phoenix 1980, cat. no. 46. For another example, see New York 1989, cat. no. 289.

3   Bartholomew 1985, pp. 23–24.

4   Personal communication from Terese Bartholomew to Claudia Brown, 13 July 2000.

5   See previous note.

6   For a shaped cover of similar satin ground with its matching side fabric still in place, see Jenyns 1965, pl. 48. On the present example, the remnants of fabric mentioned in the technical analysis may be remaining portions of the fabric that would have covered the sides of the cushion. A photograph in Beijing 1983, p. 82, shows such a cover in use.

7   Accession number 978.264, Toronto 1996, cat. no. 121.

8   See an example in Newark, accession number 41.1166, published in New York, 1980a, cat. no. 44, and a similar piece offered by Spink (Spink and Son 1994, cat. no. 50), together with a cover for a throne back of the same weave and motifs, Jenyns 1965, pl. 31.

9   Spink 1999, nos. 24 and 25. Many cushion covers have appeared on the art market recently, see Spink and Son 1989 b, nos. 71–73; and Spink and Son 1991.

10   For example, see Huang 1987, fig. 120, pp. 59 and 134–135.

11   They are visible in many photographs of the Palace Museum, Beijing; see for example, Hong Kong 1982, p. 104, pl. 96.

12   See for example, Paris 1996, page 147, detail of cat. no. 23.

13   Paris 1996, p. 152, cat. no. 22; and p. 156, cat. no. 24.

14   A portrait of the Daoguang emperor and his children shows silk covered cushions behind the figures engaged in calligraphy; see Rotterdam, 1990, page 156, figure 15.

15   Tokyo 1982, p. 19.

Qing dynasty, second half of the 19th century
  Embroidered silk; pale red silk ground in tabby weave embroidered in polychrome
  silk threads and couched with bundled silk threads wrapped with paper strips faced
  with gold and other metallic substances
H. 98 cm; W. 118 cm

Two rectangular silk panels, now faded from their original bright red (a color visible where
embroidery threads are now lost), are seamed to form a larger horizontal rectangle and additional
strips of the same silk are sewn into borders to enclose the large composition representing children
at play. The central motifs show children playing in a garden setting. Two pavilions, one with
a tile floor and the other with decorative wooden balustrades, are represented among the garden
rocks, trees, and other plants typical of the garden of a Chinese scholar-official. Shades of green
(now faded almost to blue) and blue create the suggestion of gentle outcroppings of land as well
as tall, exotic, eroded rocks. Described in satin stitch with outline stitches to create finer details,
the children are represented in threads of white as well as shades of blue, red, and yellow.
Stylized cloud patterns are satin-stitched with oblique stitches in the topmost portion. The buff
brown threads which once defined the tree at the right are now nearly gone.

The finely worked border patterns include couched metal threads representing the double
happiness symbol (*shuangxi*), often a wedding symbol denoting wishes for a couple's long and
happy life together. The characters of the left and right borders are couched in gold wrapped
threads; those at the top and bottom are couched in threads apparently wrapped with silver,
now tarnished to a brownish gray. Surrounding these characters are other auspicious symbols
including flowering and fruiting gourd vines (the gourd's many seeds suggesting multiple progeny)
and bats, a visual pun for happiness. These motifs are embroidered in satin stitch with outline
stitching, often with gold-wrapped threads, to accent the details. The gourds are couched in the
metallic thread, apparently silver, now dark brownish gray.

The panel appears to have been intended to be used as a curtain or a wall hanging, and might
have been an appropriate wedding gift or part of a bride's dowry.[1] The fact that fifty boys are
shown may suggest that an accompanying panel was made showing another group of fifty.

Depiction of many children playing was in China a wish for long life and flourishing progeny.[2]
The activities of the boys at first glance appear casual but actually relate to or obliquely suggest
the accomplishments of the traditional Chinese scholar. Transplanting flowers for the garden
may suggest the gentleman's cultivation of his garden. Carrying a ewer may suggest collecting
antiquities or perhaps the drinking of wine or tea. The geese may be a reference to the famous
calligrapher Wang Xizhi (303?–361?) who is said to have taken inspiration in calligraphy
from gazing at the movement of geese. Since a wish for a family's success would include the
appointment of sons to government posts, scholarship and implied success in the civil service

exams were crucial. Terese Bartholomew has identified one standard theme of the "hundred boys" motif as a rebus for success in the examinations. As she describes it, one boy always holds up a branch of osmanthus (*guihua*). Since the name of the flower (*gui*) can be read as a pun for noble, this child becomes the noble son.[3] The blue and green colors of the garden setting as well as the strange rocks may also have been intended to suggest a theme of paradise, since in the Chinese painting tradition this was often the case.

The style and motifs of the border patterns on the Clague textile are close to those in a curtain preserved in the Liaoning Provincial Museum, said to have been presented to the court from Suzhou in the Qianlong era.[4] Similar embroidered cloths with the hundred boys motif and these same border patterns appear in a pair of bed curtains displayed in the imperial nuptial bed-chamber in the Kunning Palace.[5] Although larger in size, the red silk ground, the floral and double happiness border, and the motifs of boys at play in a garden are very close to the example in the Clague collection. Perhaps the Clague piece, too, was one of a pair of bed curtains. The double happiness motif was also applied to more formal textiles for use in the public ceremony associated with weddings, as shown in an imperial example from a Guangxu period table cover.[6]

142

[CB]

Technical analysis
Warp: orange silk; slight Z twist; single ply. Count: 40 yarns per centimeter. Condition: photo-chemical damage. *Weft*: Foundation: orange silk; no apparent twist; single bundle of fibers. Count: 23 yarns per centimeter. Condition: photo-chemical damage. *Weave*: Tabby. Ground fabric is an unbalanced tabby weave since the wefts are much heavier than the warps. Condition: Photo-chemical damage has caused faded color and splits in the structure of the woven fabric. *Dyeing*: Piece dyed. Originally the ground fabric was red. *Selvages*: Weave: Unbalanced tabby weave. Width: Not discernible as warp yarns in selvage are identical to warps in ground fabric. Location: At least two places. They are on a folded under section of the two side borders. Other: Weft yarns turn around the outermost warp.

Embroidery
Threads: 1) polychrome silk; no apparent twist in the bundle of fibers; single ply. Location: used for satin stitches throughout textile. 2) Blue, black and dull gold colored silk; slight Z twist; 2-ply, S. Location: Outlines wheels, parts of the building, tree limbs. 3) bundle of orange silk fibers wrapped with gold; no apparent twist to silk fibers, gold is Z twist; single ply. Location: Thin thread found throughout the embroidery. As originally created, the gold wrapping does not completely cover the silk fibers. 4) bundle of orange silk fibers wrapped with gold; no apparent twist to silk fibers; gold wrap is S twist; single ply. Location: Heavier thread around the inside edge of the fabric borders. 5) bundle of pale yellow silk fibers wrapped with gold; no apparent twist to silk fibers, gold is Z twist; single ply. Thread is used to create pears and other shapes throughout the fabric borders. Condition: 60% of the threads have turned dark brown while the other 40% still have a bright gold look. *Stitches*: satin, laid and couched, outline.

Lining
The current lining was added around 1990.

[MWG]

1   That the custom continued into the 20th century is suggested by an example collected in Shanghai in the 1930s and donated to the Phoenix Art Museum by Dr. Pearl Tang (accession number 1998.147).

2   As discussed above (introduction), the theme was included in a seventeenth century manual of embroidery designs.

3   Bartholomew 1985, p. 34. She explains that traditionally "to pluck the *guihua* from the Moon Palace" was to pass the civil service exam with honors.

4   Yang et al 1983, plate 132.

5   Shown in many published photographs of this part of the Beijing palace. See, for example, Paris 1996, p. 12, fig. 10; Hong Kong 1982, p. 83, pl. 65; and also Beijing 1983, p. 29.

6   Paris 1996, page 239, cat. no. 108.

26 Rectangular Silk Panel with Two Dragons Confronting a Flaming Pearl

Qing dynasty, 19th century
  Embroidered silk; buff colored ground in 3/1 broken twill weave embroidered in
  polychrome silk threads and couched with bundled silk threads wrapped with paper
  strips faced with gold and other metallic substances
H. 73.5 cm; W. 64.5 cm

A buff colored silk fabric is embroidered with two large dragons symmetrically placed to either side of a large flaming jewel or pearl. The bodies of the dragons are represented by gold-wrapped threads laid and couched in shell-shaped patterns to resemble scales with silver-wrapped threads to accentuate their limbs and manes. Additional details of the manes are only indicated with some cursory satin stitches. Other details of the dragons are densely embroidered in satin stitch, using white thread for the spine and spiky tails as well as the horns and teeth. Black threads in outline and other stitches emphasize the mane and the belly and limbs, and concentric stitches in black highlight the bold eyes of the dragons. The pearl itself is represented as concentric satin stitch rings in shades of white, gray, and black with satin stitching in red and pink to suggest the flames emanating from the center of the gem. Many of the red threads have deteriorated here and in the details of the dragons' mouths. Descending above the pearl a red and white bat embroidered in satin stitch can be partially seen. These motifs float in a illusory space suggested by the open ground areas. These areas are partially filled by stylized clouds (in the shapes often called *ruyi*) and motifs from the *babao* ("eight treasures"). Colors used in these include shades of blue and red as well as gray, white, pink, and lavender. Rising below the flaming pearl is a stylized mountain emerging from highly abstract water and wave patterns. Along the mountain's perimeter, white satin stitched patterns suggest frothy spray crashing on the rock. Across the width of the textile below the dragons are wave patterns including parallel lines worked into curves, *ruyi* shaped motifs, and auspicious emblems floating among the waves. Below are diagonal stripes which meet to form a triangle under the central mountain. This patterning is based on the motifs typically used at the lower section of court robes in the late Qing dynasty. Here the stripes are formed by densely couched threads of three shades of metal-wrapped threads.

Dragon robes were normally reserved for the court and for civil and military officials of high rank. The fragmentary panel here appears to have affinities with the court robes of the late nineteenth century, especially those of the Guangxu era (1875–1908). Its unusually bold patterning, however, may suggest that this textile fragment may once have formed part of a theater robe, a context in which court dress would have been imitated for the purpose of dramatic spectacle. Theater costumes for actors playing the roles of generals, as well as those playing the parts of emperors, empresses, and high ranking officials, would have employed the imperial imagery of dragons (four and five claws) as seen here.[1] Since embroidered motifs are cut off at the edges, it is likely that this fragment was cut from a larger piece. The shape of the fragment and its embroidered ribbon border suggests that it was used as a hanging, perhaps a curtain. Another possibility may be that the piece was intended as a wall decoration. This could account

144

26

for the boldness of patterning meant to be seen from a distance. The imagery of dragons and clouds above stylized mountains and waves may be most familiar from the dragon robes but its use in architectural decoration is widespread, for example in the stone imperial walkways of the Forbidden City.[2]

[CB]

Technical analysis
Warp: Gold colored silk; Z twist; no ply (bundled yarns not twisted together). Count: 16 yarns per centimeter. *Weft*: gold colored silk; Z twist; single ply. Count: 40 yarns per centimeter. *Weave*: 3/1 broken twill. *Dyeing*: undetermined. *Selvages*: none remaining.

Embroidery
Threads: 1) Polychrome silk; slight S twist; no ply (bundled yarns not twisted together). 2) very heavy, white silk yarn wrapped with gold; S twist; 3-ply, Z. Wrapping: Z. Gold is adhered to gray/brown paper substrate. 3) very heavy white silk with metallic wrap; S twist; 3-ply, Z. Wrapping: Z. This thread is identical to the previous thread except the metallic wrap is a flat dark gray color. The metal is adhered to a gray/brown paper substrate. *Stitches*: satin, laid and couched, outline.

Commentary
Black ink outlines the areas to be embroidered. Some embroidery has deteriorated so that the ink shows.

[MWG]

1   For some examples of theater costumes of the Guangxu period, see Melbourne 1988, cat. nos. 84, 85, and 96.

2   See for example, Paris 1996, p.28, fig. 24. Also a wall hanging with dragon motifs appears in a photograph of the imperial kitchen, same source, p. 54, fig. 42. A panel similar to the Clague example was used a backdrop for photographs taken in Tibet in the 1920s (Aris 1992, plates 8.11 and 8.13).

Qing dynasty, late 19th century
 Embroidered silk; red ground in five-end satin weave embroidered in polychrome
 silk threads and couched with bundled silk threads wrapped with paper strips faced
 with gold and other metallic substances
H. 67 cm; W. 94 cm

This red satin (slightly faded from its original bright red, perhaps dyed with synthetic aniline 145
dyes), still rich with its palette of gold, green, and purple couching, once was more splendid
still with more than 140 reflective metal (apparently copper) sequins stitched within its border
motifs of lattice work and blossoms and its central roundel of a mythical lion and two cubs
playing with ribboned and brocaded balls. The gold wrapped threads are laid and couched in
parallel spiraling forms to capture the spirit of a large-headed lion with a powerful anatomy.
The green and purple colors, resulting from a loose wrapping of gold over bright colored silk
fibers, are used to suggest the curls of the mane and plume-like tail of the lion. Details of the
teeth and eyes are added in satin stitch. The two smaller animals are portrayed in a similar
manner, with the illusion of a mother and two cubs, one on either side, checked by the formality
of the scrolling ribbons that form a roundel or medallion in the center of the panel. The center
motifs are further emphasized by a margin of blank silk creating roughly the shape of an
ellipse. The corners are then filled with gold wrapped threads laid and couched in squared spirals,
a motif derived from ancient bronzes and jades, and interlaced with blossoms and leafy vines.

Although the original function of the panel is not known, its size and its weight (due to the
heavy metal-wrapped threads) suggest that it would have been mounted for use as a wall hanging
or curtain. The similarity of the border designs to furniture patterns would seem to confirm
this. Although the panel does not retain woven selvages, the pattern suggests a complete unit
of decoration. By this time, probably the second half of the nineteenth century, or even later,
the weaving of the ground fabric was accomplished separately and the ornamentation of the
finished piece was wholly a later process done in needlework.

The motif of the lion and cubs stems from the ancient world's use of the lion as a protector of
the throne. The throne of the historical Buddha, himself of royal lineage, was often flanked by
lions, hence the term Buddhistic lion (lions of "fuo" [Buddhism], a term sometimes rendered
as "foo dogs"). The use of the motif expanded greatly in the Ming and Qing dynasties, and the
animal became a decorative theme. Its legacy as a guardian remained and its use here may suggest
that this panel was made as a gift for an important family occasion.[1]

[CB]

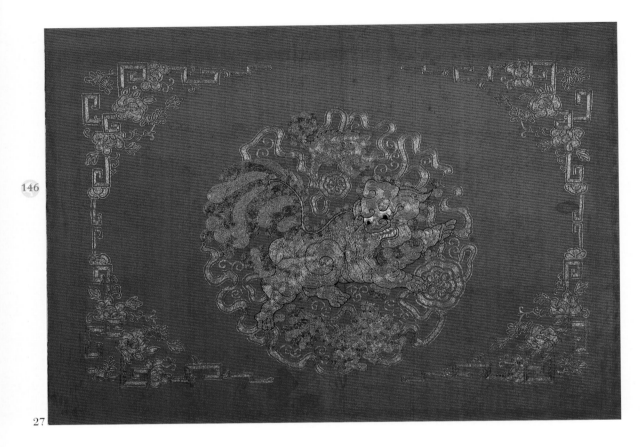

146

27

Technical analysis

Warp: pink silk (faded from red); no apparent twist; single ply. Count: 20 yarns per centimeter. Warp yarns are approximately 4 times the diameter of weft yarns. *Weft*: pink silk (faded from red); slight Z twist; single ply. Count: 48 yarns per centimeter. *Weave*: 5 end satin. Condition: Adhesive is on surface of textile on all four edges. *Dyeing*: Yarn dyed. *Selvages*: none remaining.

Embroidery

Threads: 1) heavy, pale gold silk thread wrapped with gold leaf on white paper substrate; Z twist; 5-ply S. 2) purple and green silk, slight Z twist; 2-ply, S. 3) black, orange, green and white silk; no twist (bundle of silk fibers); no ply. *Stitches*: Laid and couched, outline and satin stitches.

Embellishments: Four metal sequins (copper in color) remain but needle holes and changes in fabric color indicate that previously over 140 sequins decorated the textile.

[MWG]

1   On the many occasions for gifts of textiles, see Clunas 1997-8, p. 8.

28 Three Rectangular Silk Panels with Motifs of Antiquities and Calligraphy

Qing dynasty to early Republican period, late 19th to early 20th century
  Embroidered silk; darkened white ground in 3/1 broken twill weave, embroidered
  with polychrome silk threads
H. approx. 33 cm; W. approx. 44 cm

Three rectangular panels of 3/1 broken twill silk were prepared by darkening the ground color to achieve a background of antique white. Black outlines were added, either by painting or possibly by printing, to mark areas for the embroiderer to follow in satin stitch embroidery. In each of the three compositions short texts introduce and comment on the motifs drawn from ancient inscriptions. The first (28A) depicts the molded ends of roof tiles, probably based on rubbings of the actual tiles. The inscription at lower right reads: "Roof tiles of the Qin and Han dynasties." The round outer surfaces of two ceramic eave tiles are then represented in satin stitch embroidery, one with spiral motifs in shades of blue, and the other with four seal-script characters in yellowish brown. The legend can be rendered as "Boundless Heaven." At upper left an additional inscription in black satin stitch imitating brush-written semi-cursive script further glosses the archaic characters, "'Boundless heaven', in four characters, [forms] the text of the edged roof tile." The second panel (28B) begins at the right with vertical lines of calligraphy which render in semi cursive script the legends of a half-round eave tile and two impressed bricks shown at center and left. At a diagonal across the composition, embroidered in shades of gray and brown silk threads in satin stitch, is an elongated inscribed brick, with characters reading, "Ten thousand years of wealth and prosperity." As if behind it is a half-round brick, reading in seal script, "Wealth." At left, as if cut off by weathering and by the frame of the compositions, is embroidered in shades of blue and green a brick in the upper left corner, inscribed "Made at Tongque Palace," and picturing a horse in reddish brown. The third panel (28C) opens with the caption, embroidered in black to resemble clerical script, "Inscription of the Zhou Bao *fu* vessel." Below this, in bronze-script characters is the inscription from the Zhou dynasty bronze, "Self-made *fu* vessel, generations of descendants should use and cherish it forever." Balancing the composition on the left are two roundels representing roof tiles. The round tile reads, in seal script characters, "Longevity." As if behind it, there is another round tile, inscribed again in seal script: "Shanglin [Palace]." Above, in lines complementing these round shapes is embroidered in black silk threads the inscription, "Han roof tiles. The four characters 'Yannian yi shou (longevity)' [appear]... the Weiyang Palace had 'Yannian' tiles."

The references are to architecture of the Qin (221–207 B.C.) and Han period (206 B.C.–A.D. 220) and to a ceremonial bronze vessel of the shape called a *fu* from the Zhou dynasty (c. 1050–256 B.C.). The Weiyang palace (Weiyanggong) was built by Han emperor Gaozu and inaugurated in 198 B.C.[1] The Shanglin park was first built by Qin Shih Huangdi, and later renovated by Han emperor Wu in 138 B.C. Both were located in the southwest sector of Chang'an, modern Xi'an. The Tongque palace was commissioned in 210–213 by the famous late Han general Cao Cao (155–220).

In each of these motifs the colors of the threads—black, blue gray, peach, gray, rust, all muted colors—are, like the background, chosen to complement the theme of antiquities, and the texts selected for the embroidered calligraphy in semi-cursive script are complementary in sentiment to the archaistic texts depicted. The fact that in each case the motifs have become flat and two-dimensional, with no impression of their bulk as actual three-dimensional bricks and tiles, suggests that they were drawn from rubbings of ceramic roof tiles and other inscribed building materials of the Han dynasty. Such rubbings would have been widely published as China entered the modern period and interest in her ancient past intensified. As Lothar Ledderose[2] and others have pointed out, modern archaeology inherited the spirit of epigraphical studies (*jin shi xue*) which flourished in nineteenth century China. Inscriptions on bronzes (*jin wen*) and inscribed texts on stone became models for calligraphers. Pottery inscriptions (*tao wen*) were regarded with interest and began to be collected seriously at least by the second half of the nineteenth century.[3] These interests inspired new experimentation with ancient calligraphic styles and added new elements to the tradition of picturing collected antiquities (see number 14). The three panels in the Clague collection incorporate images similar to those found in Chinese *trompe-l'oeil* painting of the late nineteenth century.[4] These similarities support a date for these textiles in the late nineteenth or early twentieth century.

148

[translations by An-yi Pan]

[CB]

Technical analysis
Warp: Off white silk; slight S twist; 2-ply, Z. Count: 30 yarns per centimeter. *Weft*: Foundation: off white silk; Z twist; 2-ply. Count: 120 yarns per centimeter. *Weave*: 3/1 Broken twill. *Selvages*: none remaining.

Embroidery
Threads: Polychrome (black, blue gray, peach, gray, rust) silk; bundle of silk yarns with no apparent twist. Black ink was used to outline motifs then filled in with embroidery. Additional painted and/or printed areas. *Stitches*: satin.

Commentary
Each of these three textiles was prepared in an identical procedure. A rectangle of gold was painted or printed on off white silk fabric. Black ink was used to outline a design on the fabric surface. Satin stitch embroidery was executed to fill in between the ink lines. Previously the textiles had a multi-layered fabric border on all four sides.

[MWG]

1   For descriptions of the Weiyang palace and Shanglin park, see Wang
    Zhongshu 1982, pp. 4-5, and 8-9. Wang mentions roof tiles
    impressed "Shanglin" as the most conspicuous remains of the
    palaces at Shanglin. Hong Kong 1982 cites Tongque terrace as
    commissioned by Cao Cao in 210-213. For further description and
    analysis of the Weiyang Palace, see Steinhardt 1990, pp. 56-60.
2   See Ledderose, "Calligraphy at the Close of the Chinese Empire,"
    in *Phoebus* 8 (1998), pp. 196-199. Similar interests are found in
    painting; see Chuang Shen 1994.
4   Wilkinson 1998, p. 426.
5   See, for example, paintings dated to the 1880s, in Berliner 1992,
    especially fig. 13.

与天
君極の
邊字有
几三
同几
也又

秦漢
之瓦
省々

万歲富贵甄瓶甎彤瓦
龙鼠甘毛善
秦萬年

Bibliography

Alsop
1984   Ian Alsop. "Five Dated Nepalese Metal Sculptures." *Artibus Asiae* 45, no. 2/3 (1984), pp. 207–216.

American Fabrics Magazine
1972   Editorial Board of American Fabrics Magazine. *AF Encyclopedia of Textiles.* 2nd ed. Englewood Cliffs, New Jersey, 1972.

Asian Art Museum
1985   Terese Tse Bartholomew. *The Hundred Flowers: Botanical Motifs in Chinese Art.* Exh. cat., Asian Art Museum of San Francisco, 1985.

Aris
1992   Michael Aris. *Lamas, Princes, and Brigands: Joseph Rock's Photographs of the Tibetan Borderlands of China.* Exh. cat., China House Gallery, China Institute in America. New York, 1992.

Barnett
1995   Cherry Barnett. "Chinese Textiles: Technique, Design and Patterns of Use." *Arts of Asia* 25, no. 6 (November–December 1995), pp. 137–143.

Barrett
1998   J. May Lee Barrett. "Tibetan Costumes and Ceremonial Textiles at the Newark Museum, New Jersey." *The Asian Art Newspaper* (October 1998), p. 21.

Bartholomew
1985   Terese Tse Bartholomew. "Botanical Puns in Chinese Art from the Collection of the Asian Art Museum of San Francisco." *Orientations* 16, no. 9 (September 1985), pp. 18–34.

Bartholomew
1991   Terese Tse Bartholomew. "Sino-Tibetan Art of the Qianlong Period from the Asian Art Museum of San Francisco." *Orientations* 22, no. 6 (June 1991), pp. 34–45.

Beijing
1983   Gugong Bowuyuan (The Palace Museum). *Zijincheng dihou shenghuo* [Life of the Emperors and Empresses in the Forbidden City]. Beijing, 1983. [in Chinese]

Berger
1989   Patricia Berger. "A Stitch in Time: Speculations on the Origin of Needlelooping." *Orientations* 20, no. 8 (August 1989), pp. 45–53. Reprinted in **Orientations 1998**, pp. 39–47.

Berger and Bartholomew
1995   Patricia Berger, Terese Tse Bartholomew, et al. *Mongolia: The Legacy of Chinggis Khan.* London and New York, 1995.

Berinstein
1999   Dorothy Berinstein, "Hunts, Processions, and Telescopes: A Painting of an Imperial Hunt by Lang Shining (Giuseppe Castiglione)." *Res* 35 (spring 1999), pp. 170–184.

Berlin
1985   *Europa und die Kaiser von China.* Exh. cat. Berlin Fespiel GmbH, 1985. [in German]

Berliner
1992   Nancy Berliner. "The 'Eight Brokens': Chinese Trompe-l'oeil Painting." *Orientations* 23, no. 2 (February 1992), pp. 61–70.

Bray
1997   Francesca Bray. *Technology and Gender: Fabrics of Power in Late Imperial China.* Berkeley, 1997.

Brook
1998   Timothy Brook. *The Confusions of Pleasure: Commerce and Culture in Ming China.* Berkeley, 1998.

Brown
2000   Claudia Brown. "The Amy S. Clague Collection of Chinese Textiles." *Orientations* 31, no. 2 (February 2000), pp. 34–43.

Bruce
1991   Grace Wu Bruce. *The Dr. S.Y. Yip Collection of Classic Chinese Furniture.* Hong Kong, 1991.

Bunker
1993   Emma C. Bunker. "Gold in the Ancient Chinese World: A Cultural Puzzle." *Artibus Asiae* 53, nos. 1/2 (1993), pp. 27–50.

Burnham
1980   Dorothy K. Burnham. *Warp and Weft:*
        A Textile Terminology. Toronto, 1980.
        [Adapted and expanded from Centre
        International d'Études des Textiles Anciens.
        Vocabulary of Technical Terms: Fabrics.
        Lyons, 1964.]

Burnham
1959   H. P. Burnham. *Chinese Velvets.* Toronto, 1959.

Cambridge
1996   Robert D. Mowry. *Hare's Fur, Tortoiseshell,*
        and Partridge Feathers: Chinese Brown- and
        Black-Glazed Ceramics, 400–1400. Exh. cat.,
        Harvard University Art Museums.
        Cambridge, 1996.

Cambridge
1997   Robert D. Mowry. *Worlds Within Worlds: The*
        Richard Rosenblum Collection of Chinese
        Scholars' Rocks. Exh. cat., Harvard
        University Art Museums. Cambridge, 1997.

Cammann
1948   Schuyler van R. Cammann. "Notes on the
        Origin of Chinese *K'ossu* Tapestry." *Artibus*
        Asiae 11 (1948), pp. 90–110. Reprinted in
        Orientations 20, no. 8 (August 1989),
        pp. 74–81; reprinted in **Orientations 1998**,
        pp. 68–81.

Cammann
1962   Schuyler van R. Cammann. "Embroidery
        Techniques in Old China." *Archives of the*
        Chinese Art Society of America [now *Archives*
        of Asian Art] 16 (1962), pp. 16–40.

Centre International d'Études
1964   Centre International d'Études des Textiles
        Anciens. *Vocabulary of Technical Terms:*
        Fabrics. Lyons, 1964.

Chai and Chai
1967   Ch'u Chai and Winberg Chai, eds. *Li Chi:*
        Book of Rites. 2 vols. Trans. James Legge.
        New Hyde Park, New York, 1967.

Chen
1971   Chen Zhengxiang. *Zhongguo di cansi ye*
        [The Silk Industry of China]. Hong Kong,
        1971. [In Chinese]

Chen
1979   Chen Juanjuan. "Kesi" [Tapestries]. *Gugong*
        bowuyuan yuankan 3 (1979), pp. 22–29.
        [In Chinese]

Cheng
1984   Cheng Weiji, ed. *Zhongguo fangzhi kexue*
        jishu shi, gudai bufen [A History of Chinese
        Textile Technology, ancient section]. Beijing,
        1984. [In Chinese]

Cheng
1992   Cheng Weiji, chief compiler. *History of*
        Textile Technology of Ancient China.
        New York, 1992.

Chicago
1964   Jack Sewell. *Ming-Ch'ing.* Exh. cat., The Art
        Institute of Chicago, Chicago, 1964.

Chuang
1994   Chuang Shen. "Archaeology in Late Qing
        Dynasty Painting." *Ars Orientalis* 24 (1994),
        pp. 83–104.

Clunas
1981–2 Craig Clunas. "The West Chamber: A Literary
        Theme in Chinese Porcelain Decoration."
        Transactions of the Oriental Ceramic Society
        46 (1981–2), pp. 69–86.

Clunas
1992   Craig Clunas. "The Novel *Jin Ping Mei* as a
        Source for the Study of Ming Furniture."
        Orientations 23, no. 1 (January 1992),
        pp. 60–68.

Clunas
1997–8 Craig Clunas. "Gifts and Giving in Chinese
        Art." *Transactions of the Oriental Ceramic*
        Society 62 (1997–8), pp. 1–18.

Cyrus-Zetterstrom
1995   Ulla Cyrus-Zetterstrom. *Textile Terminology.*
        Stockholm, 1995.

Dayton
1984   Clarence W. Kelley. *Chinese Gold and Silver*
        in American Collections: Tang Dynasty,
        A.D. 618–907. Exh. cat., The Dayton Art
        Institute. Dayton, Ohio, 1984.

Dayton
1990   Susan L. Huntington and John C. Huntington.
        Leaves from the Bodhi Tree: The Art of Pâla
        India (8th–12th Centuries) and Its
        International Legacy. Exh. cat., The Dayton
        Art Institute. Dayton, Ohio, Seattle, and
        London, 1990.

Delbanco
1983   Dawn Ho Delbanco. "The Romance of the
        Western Chamber: Min Qiji's Album in
        Cologne." *Orientations* 14 (June 1983),
        pp. 12–23.

Dubosc
1948   Jean-Pierre Dubosc. "A Contribution to the
        Study of Sung Tapestries." *Artibus Asiae* 11
        (1948), pp. 73–89. Reprinted in
        Orientations 20, no. 8 (August 1989),
        pp. 82–86; reprinted in **Orientations 1998**,
        pp. 76–80.

Ebrey
1999   Patricia Ebrey. "The Ritual Context of Sung
        Imperial Portraiture." In Cary Y. Liu and
        Dora C. Ching, eds. *Arts of the Sung and*
        Yüan: Ritual, Ethnicity, and Style in Painting.
        Princeton, 1999, pp. 68–93.

Ecke
1963   Gustav Ecke. *Chinese Domestic Velvets.*
        Tokyo, 1963.

Ellsworth
1996   Robert Hatfield Ellsworth. *Chinese*
        Furniture: One Hundred Examples from the
        Mimi and Raymond Hung Collection.
        New York, 1996.

Ellsworth
1997   Robert Hatfield Ellsworth. *Chinese Furniture:*
        Hardwood Examples of the Ming and Early
        Ch'ing Dynasties. Revised ed. New Fairfield,
        Connecticut, 1997.

Emery
1980   Irene Emery. *The Primary Structures of*
        Fabrics: An Illustrated Classification.
        Washington, D. C., 1980.

Fong

1992   Wen C. Fong. *Beyond Representation: Chinese Painting and Calligraphy, 8th–14th Century*. New York, 1992.

Frederic

1995   Louis Frederic. *Buddhism: Flammarion Iconographic Guides*. Paris, 1995.

Freer Gallery of Art

1972   Freer Gallery of Art. *The Freer Gallery of Art*. Vol. 1: *China*. Tokyo, 1972.

Fujian Provincial Museum

1982   Fujian sheng bowuguan [Fujian Provincial Museum]. *Fuzhou Nan Song Huang Sheng mu* [The Southern Song Tomb of Huang Sheng in Fuzhou]. Beijing, 1982. [In Chinese]

Fujioka and Hasebe

1976   Fujioka Ryōichi and Hasebe Gakuji. *Min* [Ming], *Sekai tōji zenshū* [Ceramic art of the world] series, vol. 14. Ed. The Zauho Press. Tokyo, 1976. [In Japanese]

Gansu Provincial Museum

1982   Gansu sheng bowuguan [Gansu Provincial Museum] and Zhang xian wenwuguan [Zhang County Culture Center]. "Gansu Zhang xian Yuandai Wang Shixian jiazu muzang: Jianbao zhi yi" [The Yuan-dynasty tombs of the Wang Shixian family in Zhang county, Gansu province: First brief report]. *Wenwu* 2 (1982), pp. 1–12 and n.p., pls. 1–2. [In Chinese]

Gao

1987   Gao Hanyu. *Soieries de Chine* [The Silks of China]. Paris, 1987. [In French]

Gao

1992   Gao Hanyu. *Chinese Textile Designs*. Trans. Rosemary Scott and Susan Whitfield. London, 1992.

Gao

1995   Gao Hanyu. "Technical and Artistic Development of Chinese Patterned Silk." Trans. Don J. Cohn. In Urban Council, Hong Kong, and the Oriental Ceramic Society of Hong Kong in association with the Liaoning Provincial Museum. *Jinxiu luoyi qiao tiangong / Heavens' Embroidered Cloths: One-Thousand Years of Chinese Textiles*. Exh. cat., Hong Kong Museum of Art. Hong Kong, 1995, pp. 44–49.

Garner

1979   Sir Harry Garner. *Chinese Lacquer*. London, 1979.

Garrett

1998   Valery M. Garrett. *Chinese Dragon Robes*. Oxford, 1998.

Gastinel-Coural

1996   "Beauvais: Centre of Tapestry Production," in *Dictionary of Art*, Jane Turner, editor, London and New York, 1996, volume 3, pp. 460–462.

Geijer

1951   Agnes Geijer. *Oriental Textiles in Sweden*. Copenhagen, 1951.

Geijer

1979   Agnes Geijer. *A History of Textile Art*. London, 1979.

Gluckman

1995   Dale Carolyn Gluckman. "Chinese Textiles and the Tibetan Connection." In Urban Council, Hong Kong, and the Oriental Ceramic Society of Hong Kong in association with the Liaoning Provincial Museum. *Jinxiu luoyi qiao tiangong / Heavens' Embroidered Cloths: One-Thousand Years of Chinese Textiles*. Exh. cat., Hong Kong Museum of Art. Hong Kong, 1995, pp. 24–25.

Gluckman

2000   Dale Carolyn Gluckman. "For Merit and Meditation: Selected Buddhist Textiles in the Los Angeles County Museum of Art." *Orientations* 31, no. 6 (June 2000), pp. 90–98.

Gray

1984   Basil Gray. *Sung Porcelain and Stoneware*. London, 1984.

Hasebe

1973   Hasebe Gakuji. *Tōji* [Ceramics]. *Chūgoku bijutsu* [Chinese Art in Western Collections] series, vol. 5. Ed. Akiyama Terukazu. Tokyo, 1973.

Hasebe

1977   Hasebe Gakuji. *Sō* [Song]. *Sekai tōji zenshū* [Ceramic Art of the World] series, vol. 12. Ed. The Zauho Press. Tokyo, 1977.

Hearn

1988   Maxwell Hearn. "Document and Portrait: The Southern Tour Paintings of Kangxi and Qianlong." *Phoebus* 6.1 (1988), pp. 91–131.

Heilongjiang Provincial Institute

1989   Heilongjiang sheng wenwu kaogu yenjiu suo [Heilongjiang Provincial Institute of Cultural Relics and Archaeology]. "Heilongjiang Acheng Juyuan Jindai Qiguo wangmu fajue jianbao" [Brief report on the excavation of the tomb of Prince Qi of the Jin dynasty at Juyuan, Acheng, Heilongjiang province]. *Wenwu* 10 (1989), pp. 1–10, 45 and n.p., pls. 1–4. [In Chinese]

Henss

2000   Michael Henss. "The New Tibet Museum in Lhasa." *Orientations* 31, no. 2 (February 2000), pp. 62–65.

Hollen, Saddler, and Langford

1979   Norma Hollen, Jane Saddler, and Anna L. Langford. *Textiles*. 5th ed. New York and London, 1979.

Hong

1999   Hong Zaixin with Cao Yiqiang. "Pictorial Representation and Mongol Institutions in *Khubilai Khan Hunting*." In Cary Y. Liu and Dora C. Ching, eds. *Arts of the Sung and Yüan: Ritual, Ethnicity, and Style in Painting*. Princeton, 1999, pp. 180–201.

Hong Kong

1982   Yu Zhuoyun, comp. *Zijincheng gong dian* [Palaces of the Forbidden City]. Hong Kong, 1982.

153

Hong Kong

1993   Jingdezhen Institute of Ceramic Archaeology and the Tsui Museum of Art. *Chengyao i zhen: Jingdezhen Zhushan chutu Chenghua guanyao ciqi / A Legacy of Chenghua: Imperial Porcelain of the Chenghua Reign Excavated from Zhushan, Jingdezhen.* Exh. cat., The Tsui Museum of Art. Hong Kong, 1993. [In Chinese and English]

Hong Kong

1995   Urban Council, Hong Kong, and the Oriental Ceramic Society of Hong Kong in association with the Liaoning Provincial Museum. *Jinxiu luoyi qiao tiangong / Heavens' Embroidered Cloths: One-Thousand Years of Chinese Textiles.* Exh. cat., Hong Kong Museum of Art. Hong Kong, 1995. [In Chinese and English]

Hong Kong

1987   *Tributes from Guangdong to the Qing Court.* Exh. cat., Art Gallery, The Chinese University of Hong Kong. Hong Kong, 1987.

Hsiung

1935   S.I. Hsiung. *The Romance of the Western Chamber.* London, 1935.

Hsu

1986   Hsu Wen-chin. "Fictional Scenes on Chinese Transitional Porcelain (1620–c. 1683) and Their Sources of Decoration." *Bulletin of the Museum of Far Eastern Antiquities* (Stockholm) 58 (1986), pp. 1–146.

Huang

1985   Huang Nengfu, ed. *Yin ran zhi xiu (shang)* [Printing, dyeing, weaving, and embroidery, part 1]. In *Zhongguo meishu quanji*: Part 3— *Gongyi meishu bian* [The great treasury of Chinese fine arts: Part 3—Arts and crafts], vol. 6. Beijing, 1985. [In Chinese]

Huang

1987   Huang Nengfu, ed. *Yin ran zhi xiu* (xia) [Printing, dyeing, weaving, and embroidery, part 2]. In *Zhongguo meishu quanji*: Part 3— *Gongyi meishu bian* [The great treasury of Chinese fine arts: Part 3—Arts and crafts], vol. 7. Beijing, 1987. [In Chinese]

Hummel

1943   Arthur W. Hummel, ed. *Eminent Chinese of the Ch'ing Period.* Washington D.C., 1943.

Hunan Provincial Museum

1973   Hunan sheng bowuguan [Hunan Provincial Museum]. *Changsha Mawangdui yi hao Han mu* [Han Tomb Number One at Mawangdui, Changsha]. Beijing, 1973. [in Chinese]

Indictor et al.

1988   Norman Indictor, Robert J. Koestler, C. Blair, and Anne E. Wardwell. "The Evaluation of Metal Wrappings from Medieval Textiles Using Scanning Electron Microscopy— Energy Dispersive X-Ray Spectrometry." *Textile History* 19, no. 1 (1988), pp. 3–22.

Indictor et al.

1989   Norman Indictor, Robert J. Koestler, M. Wypyski, and Anne E. Wardwell. "Metal Threads Made of Proteinaceous Substrates Examined by Scanning Electro Microscopy— Energy Dispersive X-Ray Spectrometry." *Studies in Conservation* 34 (1989), pp. 171–182.

Inner Mongolia

1987   Neimengu wenwu kaogu yanjiu suo [Inner Mongolia Institute of Cultural Relics and Archaeology]. "Liao Chenguo gongzhu fuma hezang mu fajue jianbao" [Brief report on the excavation of the tomb of the princess and her husband of the Liao state of Chen]. *Wenwu* 11 (1987), pp. 4–24, n.p., color pls. 1–2, and n.p., black-and-white plates 1–8. [In Chinese]

Jarry

1981   Madeleine Jarry. *Chinoiserie: Chinese Influence on European Decorative Art, 17th and 18th Centuries.* Fribourg, 1981.

Jenyns

1965   R. Soame Jenyns. *Chinese Art: The Minor Arts II.* New York, 1965.

Jin

1988   Jin Weinuo, ed. *Si guan bi hua* [Temple Wall Paintings]. In *Zhongguo meishu quanji — Hui hua bian* [The Great Treasury of Chinese Fine Arts: Painting], vol. 13. Beijing, 1988.

Jull and Donahue

1990   A.J. Timothy Jull and Douglas J. Donahue. "Radiocarbon Dating with Accelerators Methods and Application to Textiles." *Orientations* 21, no. 6 (June 1990), pp. 75–79. Reprinted in **Orientations 1998**, pp. 100–104.

Kadolph and Langford

1993   Sarah J. Kadolph and Anna L. Langford. *Textiles.* 8th ed. Upper Saddle River, New Jersey and Columbus, Ohio, 1993.

Kansas City

1992   Wai-kam Ho, ed. *The Century of Tung Ch'i-ch'ang 1555–1636.* 2 vols. Exh. cat., The Nelson-Atkins Museum of Art. Kansas City, 1992.

Karmay

1975   Heather Karmay. *Early Sino-Tibetan Art.* Warminster, England, 1975.

Kennedy and Maitland

1989   Alan Kennedy and Lucy Maitland. "Notes on the Use of Flat Metallic Strips in Central and East Asian Textiles." *The Bulletin of the Needle and Bobbin Club* 72, nos. 1–2 (1989), pp. 42–54.

Kerr

1991   Rose Kerr, ed. *Chinese Art and Design.* London: Victoria and Albert Museum, 1991.

Keswick

1986   Maggie Keswick. *The Chinese Garden: History, Art, and Architecture.* 2nd, rev. ed. London, 1986.

154

Kim and Lee
1974   Chewon Kim and Lena Kim Lee. *Arts of Korea.* Tokyo, New York, and San Francisco, 1974.

Ko
1994   Dorothy Ko. *Teachers of the Inner Chambers: Women and Culture in Seventeenth-Century China.* Stanford, 1994.

Kobayashi
1983   Kobayashi Hiromitsu, "Chin Kōjū no hanga katsudō (jō)" [Chen Hung-shou's illustrations to the 1639 Xixiangji—A study of late Ming pictorial woodblock prints, part 1], *Kokka* 79, no. 8 (1983), pp. 25–39. [In Japanese, with English summary]

Kohara et al.
1998   Natsuko Kohara, Yoshihiko Sasa, Kiyohiko Sakurai, and M. Uda. "A Note on the Characterization of Metal Threads in Historic Textiles Handed down by the Ainu People." *Studies in Conservation* 43 (1998), pp. 109–113.

Kossak
1998   Steve Kossak. "Early Paintings from Central Tibet in The Metropolitan Museum of Art." *Orientations* 29, no. 9 (October 1998), pp. 50–63.

Krahl
1989   Regina Krahl. "Designs on Early Chinese Textiles." *Orientations* 20, no. 8 (August 1989), pp. 62–73. Reprinted in **Orientations 1998**, pp. 56–67.

Krahl
1995   Regina Krahl. "Early Bronze Age Dress." *Orientations* 26, no. 5 (May 1995), pp. 58–61. Reprinted in **Orientations 1998**, pp. 154–157.

Krahl
1997   Regina Krahl. "Mediaeval Silks Woven in Gold: Khitan, Jürchen, Tangut, Chinese or Mongol?" *Orientations* 28, no. 4 (April 1997), pp. 45–51. Reprinted in **Orientations 1998**, pp. 181–187.

Lawrence, KS
1994   Marsha Weidner, editor. *Latter Days of the Law: Images of Chinese Buddhism, 850–1850.* Exh. cat., Spencer Museum of Art, University of Kansas. Lawrence, KS, 1994.

Ledderose
1998   Lothar Ledderose. "Calligraphy at the Close of the Chinese Empire." *Phoebus* 8 (1998), pp. 189–207.

Lee
1995   Rose Lee. "Chinese Textiles Related to Tibetan Buddhism in the Hong Kong Museum of Art." *Arts of Asia* 25, no. 4 (July–August 1995), pp. 70–79.

Levinson
1983   Susan B. Levinson. "Discovering an Important Mongol Silk Textile." *Hali* 5, no. 4 (1983), pp. 496–497.

Li
1979   Li Yiyou. "Tan Yuan Jininglu yizhi chutu de sizhiwu" [On the Silk Textiles Excavated at the Yuan-period Jininglu Site]. *Wenwu* 8 (1979), pp. 37–39. [In Chinese]

Liaoning Provincial Museum
1982   Liaoning sheng bowuguan [Liaoning Provincial Museum]. *Liaoning sheng bowuguan cang Song Yuan Ming Qing kesi* [Song, Yuan, Ming, and Qing tapestries in the collection of the Liaoning Provincial Museum, Shenyang]. Beijing, 1982. [In Chinese]

Liu
1941   Liu Dajun [also known as D. K. Lieu]. *The Silk Industry of China.* Shanghai, 1941.

Liu
1995   Liu Xinru. "Silks and Religions in Eurasia c. A.D. 600–1200." *Journal of World History* 6, no. 1 (1995), pp. 25–48.

Liu and Ching
1999   Cary Y. Liu and Dora C. Ching, eds. *Arts of the Sung and Yüan: Ritual, Ethnicity, and Style in Painting.* Princeton, 1999.

London
1990   Roderick Whitfield and Anne Farrer. *Caves of the Thousand Buddhas: Chinese Art from the Silk Route.* Exh. cat., The British Museum. London, 1990.

Lopez
1998   Donald S. Lopez, Jr. *Prisoners of Shangri-La: Tibetan Buddhism and the West.* Chicago and London, 1998.

Lu
1999   Tracey Lie-dan Lu. "From Barkcloth Beating to Silk Weaving: The Textile Industry from Prehistory to the Western Han Dynasty in South China." *The Textile Museum Journal 1997–1998* 37–38 (1999), pp. 61–70.

Lu and Han
1985   Ju Jiugao and Han Wei. *Tangdai jinyin qi* [Gold and Silver of the Tang dynasty]. Beijing, 1985 [In Chinese, with English summary]

Lubo-Lesnichenko
1995   Evgeny Lubo-Lesnichenko. "Concerning the Chronology and Ornamentation of Han Period Textiles." *Orientations* 26, no. 5 (May 1995), pp. 62–69. Reprinted in **Orientations 1998**, pp. 158–65.

Machida
1988   Machida shiritsu kokusai hanga bijutsukan [Machida International Print Museum]. *Chūgoku kodai hanga ten: Chūgoku hanga nisen nen ten, dai san bu* [Exhibition of Ancient Chinese Woodblock Prints: Third section of the exhibition "Two thousand Years of Chinese Printing"]. Exh. cat., Machida International Print Museum. Machida, Tokyo, 1988. [In Japanese]

Malagò
1988   Amina Malagò. "The Origin of *Kesi*, The Chinese Silk Tapestry." *Annali di ca'Foscari,* Rivista della Facolta di Lingue e Letterature Straniere dell'Universita di Venezia, vol. 27, no. 3 (1988), pp. 279–297.

Malagò
1997–8 Amina Malagò. "Supposedly Late Zhou Origin of Tapestry Technique in China." *Oriental Art* 43, no. 4 (Winter 1997–98), pp. 49–56.

155

Malone
1934   Carroll Brown Malone, *History of the Peking Summer Palaces under the Ch'ing Dynasty*, New York, 1966 (reprint of Urbana, 1934 edition).

Marcuson
1994   Alan Marcuson, ed. *The 1994 Hali Annual*. London, 1994.

Melbourne
1988   Mae Anna Pang. *Dragon Emperor: Treasures from the Forbidden City*. Exh. cat., National Gallery of Victoria. Melbourne, 1988.

Milan
1993   Mikhail Piotrosky. *Lost Empire of the Silk Road: Buddhist Art from Khara Khoto (X–XIIth Century)*. Exh. cat., Villa Favorita, Fondazione Thyssen-Bornemisza. Milan, 1993.

Milhaupt
1992   Terry Milhaupt. "The Chinese Textile and Costume Collection at The Metropolitan Museum of Art." *Orientations* 23, no. 4 (April 1992), pp. 72–78. Reprinted in **Orientations 1998**, pp. 111–117.

Mirviss
1995   Joan B. Mirviss, with John T. Carpenter and an introduction by Bruce Brooks Pfeiffer. *The Frank Lloyd Wright Collection of Surimono*. New York and Phoenix, 1995.

Mowry
1981   Robert D. Mowry. *Handbook of the Mr. and Mrs. John D. Rockefeller 3rd Collection*. New York, 1981.

Murata and Fujieda
1955   Murata Jirō and Fujieda Akira, eds. *Kyoyōkan (Chu-yung-kuan)* [The Juyong Gate]. 2 vols. Kyoto, 1955. [In Japanese, with English summary]

Myers
1989   Myrna Myers. "Silk Furnishings of the Ming and Qing Dynasties." In Krishna Riboud, ed. *In Quest of Themes and Skills—Asian Textiles*. Bombay, 1989, pp. 126–140.

National Palace Museum
1970   Guoli Gugong bowuyuan [National Palace Museum]. *Guoli Gugong bowuyuan kesi zixiu* [Tapestries and Embroideries in the Collection of the National Palace Museum, Taipei]. Tokyo, 1970. [In Chinese, Japanese, and English]

National Palace Museum
1971   National Palace Museum, Taipei. *Masterpieces of Tibetan Buddhist Altar Fittings in the National Palace Museum*. Taipei, 1971. [in Chinese, Japanese, and English]

National Palace Museum
1981   National Palace Museum, Taipei. *Masterpieces of Chinese Silk Tapestry and Embroidery in the National Palace Museum*. Taipei, 1981. [in Chinese, Japanese, and English]

New York
1931   Alan Priest and Pauline Simmons. *Chinese Textiles: An Introduction to the Study of Their History, Sources, Technique, Symbolism, and Use. Occasioned by the Exhibition of Chinese Court Robes and Accessories.* Exh. cat., The Metropolitan Museum of Art. New York, 1931.

New York
1945   Alan Priest. *Costumes from the Forbidden City*. Exh. cat., The Metropolitan Museum of Art. New York, 1945 (reprinted by Arno Press, 1974).

New York
1971   Jean Mailey. *Chinese Silk Tapestry: K'o-ssu— From Private and Museum Collections*. Exh. cat., China House Gallery, China Institute in America. New York, 1971.

New York
1978   Jean Mailey. *Embroidery of Imperial China*. Exh. cat., China House Gallery, China Institute in America. New York, 1978.

New York
1980 a   Valrae Reynolds and Yen Fen Pei. *Chinese Art from The Newark Museum*. Exh. cat., China House Gallery, China Institute in America. New York, 1980.

New York
1980 b   James C.Y. Watt. *Chinese Jades from Han to Ch'ing*. Exh. cat., The Asia Society. New York, 1980.

New York
1983   Stephen Little. *Chinese Ceramics of the Transitional Period, 1620–1683*. Exh. cat., China House Gallery, China Institute in America. New York, 1983.

New York
1985   Sören Edgren with Tsuen-Hsuin Tsien, Wang Fang-yu and Wan-go H. C. Weng. *Chinese Rare Books in American Collections*. Exh. cat., China House Gallery, China Institute in America. New York, 1985.

New York
1987   Chu-tsing Li and James C.Y. Watt, editors. *The Chinese Scholar's Studio: Artistic Life in the Late Ming Period*. Exh. cat., The Asia Society Galleries. New York, 1987.

New York
1989   Helmut Brinker and Albert Lutz. *Chinese Cloisonné: The Pierre Uldry Collection*. Trans. Susanna Swoboda. Exh. cat., The Asia Society Galleries. New York, 1989.

New York
1991   James C.Y. Watt and Barbara Brennan Ford. *East Asian Lacquer: The Florence and Herbert Irving Collection*. Exh. cat., The Metropolitan Museum of Art. New York, 1991.

New York
1995   Curtis, Julia B. *Chinese Porcelains of the Seventeenth Century: Landscapes, Scholars' Motifs and Narratives*. Exh. cat., China House Gallery, China Institute in America. New York, 1995.

New York
1996   Wen C. Fong and James C.Y. Watt, eds. *Possessing the Past: Treasures from the National Palace Museum, Taipei.* Exh. cat., The Metropolitan Museum of Art. New York, 1996.

New York
1997   James C.Y. Watt and Anne E. Wardwell, with an essay by Morris Rossabi. *When Silk Was Gold: Central Asian and Chinese Textiles.* Exh. cat., The Metropolitan Museum of Art. New York, 1997.

New York
1998   Howard Rogers, ed. *China: Five Thousand Years—Innovation and Transformation in the Arts.* Exh. cat., Solomon R. Guggenheim Museum. New York, 1998.

Nickel
1991   Helmut Nickel. "The Dragon and the Pearl." *Metropolitan Museum of Art Journal* 26 (1991), pp. 138–146.

Ogasawara
1989   Sae Ogasawara. "Chinese Fabrics of the Song and Yuan Dynasties Preserved in Japan." *Orientations* 20, no. 8 (August 1989), pp. 32–44. Reprinted in **Orientations 1998**, pp. 26–38.

Orientations
1998   Orientations Magazine Ltd. *Chinese and Central Asian Textiles: Selected Articles from Orientations 1983–1997.* Reprint publication. Hong Kong, 1998.

Pal
1983   Pratapaditya Pal. *Art of Tibet: A Catalogue of the Los Angeles County Museum of Art Collection.* Los Angeles, 1983.

Pal
1994   Pratapaditya Pal. "An Early Ming Embroidered Masterpiece." *Christie's Magazine* (May 1994), pp. 62–63.

Pal and Meech-Pekarik
1988.   Pratapaditya Pal and Julia Meech-Pekarik. *Buddhist Book Illuminations.* Hurstpierpoint, England, 1988.

Pan
1979   Pan Xingrong. "Yuan Jininglu gucheng chutu de jiaocang sizhiwu ji qita" [Silk Cloths and Other Objects Recovered at the Site of the Ancient City of Jininglu of the Yuan Dynasty]. *Wenwu* 8 (1979), pp. 32–25. [In Chinese]

Paris
1996   *La Cité interdite: Vie publique et privée des empereurs de Chine, 1644–1911.* Exh. cat., Musée du Petit Palais. Paris, 1996.

Phoenix
1980   Claudia Brown. *Chinese Cloisonné: The Clague Collection.* Exh. cat., Phoenix Art Museum. Phoenix,1980.

Phoenix
1987   Claudia Brown and Donald N. Rabiner. *The Robert H. Clague Collection: Chinese Glass of the Qing Dynasty, 1644–1911.* Exh. cat., Phoenix Art Museum. Phoenix, 1987.

Phoenix
1993   Robert D. Mowry. China's Renaissance in Bronze: *The Robert H. Clague Collection of Later Chinese Bronzes, 1100–1900.* Exh. cat., Phoenix Art Museum. Phoenix, 1993.

Pirazzoli-t'Serstevens
1988   "The Emperor Qianlong's European Palaces." *Orientations* 19, no. 11 (November, 1988), pp. 61–71.

Polonyi
1970   P. Polonyi. "Chinese Sutra Covers in the Collection of the Ferenc Hopp Museum of Eastern Asiatic Arts in Budapest." *Acta Orientalia Academiae Scientiarum Hungaricae* 23, no. 1 (1970), pp. 85–106.

Providence
1992   Susan Anderson Hay et al. *Patterns and Poetry: Nō Robes from the Lucy Truman Aldrich Collection at the Museum of Art, Rhode Island School of Design.* Exh. cat., Museum of Art, Rhode Island School of Design. Providence, 1992.

Rawski
1998   Evelyn S. Rawski. *The Last Emperors: A Social History of Qing Imperial Institutions.* Berkeley, 1998.

Rawson
1984   Jessica Rawson. *Chinese Ornament: The Lotus and the Dragon.* London, 1984.

Reynolds
1995 a   Valrae Reynolds. "The Silk Road: From China to Tibet—And Back." *Orientations* 26, no. 5 (May 1995), pp. 50–57. Reprinted in **Orientations 1998**, pp. 146–153.

Reynolds
1995 b   Valrae Reynolds. "'Thousand Buddhas' Capes and Their Mysterious Role in Sino-Tibetan Trade and Liturgy." In Urban Council, Hong Kong, and the Oriental Ceramic Society of Hong Kong in association with the Liaoning Provincial Museum. *Jinxiu luoyi qiao tiangong / Heavens' Embroidered Cloths: One-Thousand Years of Chinese Textiles.* Exh. cat., Hong Kong Museum of Art. Hong Kong, 1995, pp. 32–37.

Reynolds
1997   Valrae Reynolds. "Buddhist Silk Textiles: Evidence for Patronage and Ritual Practice in China and Tibet." *Orientations* 28, no. 4 (April 1997), pp. 52–63. Reprinted in **Orientations 1998**, pp. 188–199.

Rhie, Thurman, and Bigelow
1991   Marilyn Rhie, Robert A. F. Thurman, and John Bigelow. *Wisdom and Compassion: The Sacred Art of Tibet.* New York, 1991.

Riboud
1989   Krishna Riboud, ed. *In Quest of Themes and Skills—Asian Textiles.* Bombay, 1989.

Riboud
1995   Krishna Riboud. "Early Chinese Textiles: A Cultural Continuum—A New Group of Liao and Jin Dynasty Silks." *Hali* 17, no. 4 (August–September 1995), pp. 92–105 and appendix.

Riboud and Vial
1970   Krishna Riboud and Gabriel Vial. *Tissus de Touen-Houang conservés au Musée Guimet et à la Bibliothèque nationale* [Fabrics from Dunhuang preserved in the Musée Guimet and in the National Library, Paris]. Mission Paul Pelliot: Documents archéologiques, 13. Paris, 1970. [In French]

Riboud et al.
1996   Krishna Riboud et al. *Soieries bouddhiques chinoises, XIVe–XVIIIe Siècle / Chinese Buddhist Silks, 14th–18th Century*. Paris, 1996. [In French and English]

Riboud et al.
1998   Krishna Riboud et al. *Samit et Lampas: Motifs indiens / Samit and Lampas: Indian Motifs*. Paris, 1998. [In French and English]

Riccardi-Cubitt
1996   Monique Riccardi-Cubitt. "Chinoiserie," in *Dictionary of Art*, Jane Turner, editor, London and New York, 1996, volume 7, pp. 165–169.

Richardson
1993   Hugh Richardson. *Ceremonies of the Lhasa Year*. London, 1993.

Riddell
1979   Sheila Riddell. *Dated Chinese Antiquities, 600–1650*. London and Boston, 1979.

Riegl
1992   Alois Riegl. *Problems of Style: Foundations for a History of Ornaments*. Princeton, 1992.

Rogers
1988   Howard Rogers. "For Love of God: Castiglione at the Court of Qianlong." *Phoebus* 6.1 (1988), pp. 141–160.

Rotterdam
1990   De Verboden Stad: *Hofcultuur van de Chinese keizers (1644–1911)* [The Forbidden City: Court Culture of the Chinese Emperors (1644–1911)]. Exh. cat., Museum Boymans-van Beuningen, Rotterdam, 1990. [in Dutch and English]

San Francisco
1983   René-Yvon Lefebvre d'Argencé, ed. *Treasures from the Shanghai Museum: Six Thousand Years of Chinese Art*. Exh. cat., Asian Art Museum of San Francisco. San Francisco, 1983.

San Francisco
1987   Lucy Lim, ed. *Stories from China's Past: Han Dynasty Pictorial Tomb Reliefs and Archaeological Objects from Sichuan Province, People's Republic of China*. Exh. cat., The Chinese Culture Foundation of San Francisco. San Francisco, 1987.

Sheng
1995   Angela Sheng. "Chinese Silk Tapestry: A Brief Social Historical Perspective of Its Early Development." *Orientations* 26, no. 5 (May 1995), pp. 70–75. Reprinted in **Orientations 1998**, pp. 166–171, with addendum on p. 225.

Shih
1976   Shih Min-hsiung. *The Silk Industry in Ch'ing China*. Trans. E-tu Zen Sun. *Michigan Abstracts of Chinese and Japanese Works on Chinese History* series, no. 5. Ann Arbor, 1976.

Sickman
1957   Laurence Sickman. "Chinese Silver of the Yuan Dynasty." *Archives of the Chinese Art Society of America* [now *Archives of Asian Art*] 11 (1957), pp. 80–83.

Simcox
1989   Jacqueline Simcox. "Early Chinese Textiles: Silks from the Middle Kingdom." *Hali* 11, no. 1 (February 1989), pp. 16–33 and 119, appendix.

Simcox
1994   Jacqueline Simcox. "Chinese Textiles: Tracing the Dragon—The Stylistic Development of Designs in Early Chinese Textiles." In Alan Marcuson, ed. *The 1994 Hali Annual*. London, 1994, pp. 34–47, 245.

Simmons
1948   Pauline Simmons. *Chinese Patterned Silks*. New York, 1948.

Simmons
1950   Pauline Simmons. "Crosscurrents in Chinese Silk History." *Metropolitan Museum of Art Bulletin*, n.s. 9 (November 1950), pp. 87–96.

Simmons
1956   Pauline Simmons. "Some Recent Developments in Chinese Textile Studies." *Bulletin of the Museum of Far Eastern Antiquities* (Stockholm) 28 (1956), pp. 19–44.

Sirén
1926   Osvald Sirén. *The Imperial Palaces of Peking*. 1926. [in French and English]

Sonday and Maitland
1989   Milton Sonday and Lucy Maitland. "The Asian Embroidery Technique: Detached Looping." *Orientations* 20, no. 8 (August 1989), pp. 54–61. Reprinted in **Orientations 1998**, pp. 48–55.

Soothill
1937   William Edward Soothill. *A Dictionary of Chinese Buddhist Terms*. London, 1937.

Sperling
1979   Elliott Sperling. "The 5th Karma-pa and Some Aspects of the Relationship Between Tibet and the Early Ming," in Michael Aris and Aung San Suu Kyi, eds., *Tibetan Studies in Honour of Hugh Richardson, Proceedings of the International Seminar on Tibetan Studies*. Oxford, 1979, pp. 280–289.

Spink and Son
1989 a   Paul Champkins, Jacqueline Simcox, et al. *The Minor Arts of China* IV. Dealer's cat., Spink and Son. London, 1989.

Spink and Son
1989 b   Francesca Galloway and Jacqueline Simcox. *The Art of Textiles*. Dealer's cat., Spink and Son. London, 1989.

Spink and Son
1991   G.W. Dickinson. *Chinese Imperial Cushions*. Dealer's cat., Spink and Son and Linda Wrigglesworth, 1991.

Spink and Son
1994   Jacqueline Simcox. *Chinese Textiles.*
        Dealer's cat., Spink. London, 1994.

Spink and Son
1999   Antonia Tozer. *Threads of Imagination:*
        Central Asian and Chinese Silks from the
        12th to the 19th Century. Dealer's cat.,
        Spink. London, 1999.

Stein
1912   Sir Marc Aurel Stein. *Ruins of Desert Cathay:*
        Personal Narrative of Explorations in Central
        Asia and Westernmost China. London, 1912
        (New York reprint, 1968).

Steinhardt
1990   Nancy Shatzman Steinhardt. *Chinese*
        Imperial City Planning. Honolulu, 1990.

Taipei
1977   Guoli Gugong bowuyuan [National Palace
        Museum]. *Ming Chenghua ciqi tezhan*
        [Exhibition of Porcelain from the Chenghua
        Reign of the Ming dynasty]. Exh. cat., National
        Palace Museum. Taipei, 1977. [In Chinese]

Textile Gallery
1998   Michael Franses. *Textile Art from the Silk*
        Road: Part I—Silk Embroideries, Brocades,
        and Tapestries, AD 900–1600. Dealer's cat.,
        The Textile Gallery, London, at MD Flacks
        Ltd., New York. London, 1998.

Thomas
1935   Mary Thomas. *Mary Thomas's Dictionary of*
        Embroidery Stitches. New York, 1935.

Tímár-Balázsy and Eastop
1998   Agnes Tímár-Balázsy and Dinah Eastop.
        Chemical Principles of Textile Conservation.
        Oxford and Boston, 1998.

Tokyo National Museum
1994   Tōkyō kokuritsu hakubutsukan [Tokyo
        National Museum]. *Chūgoku no tōji:*
        Tokubetsuten [Chinese Ceramics: A Special
        Exhibition]. Exh. cat., Tokyo National
        Museum. Tokyo, 1994. [In Japanese]

Toronto
1996   *Royal Ontario Museum: The T. T. Tsui*
        Galleries of Chinese Art. Toronto, 1996.

Tung
1980   Rosemary Jones Tung. *A Portrait of Lost Tibet.*
        New York, 1980.

Vainker
1996   Shelagh J. Vainker. "Silk of the Northern Song:
        Reconstructing the Evidence." In Jill Tilden,
        ed. *Silk and Stone: The Third Hali Annual.*
        London, 1996, pp. 160–175, 196–197.

Vedlich
1979   Joseph Vedlich. *The Prints of the Ten*
        Bamboo Studio. Fribourg, 1979.

Vollmer
1977   John E. Vollmer. *In the Presence of the*
        Dragon Throne: Ch'ing Dynasty Costume
        (1644–1911) in the Royal Ontario Museum.
        Toronto, 1977.

Vollmer
1982   John E. Vollmer. "Chinese Tapestry Weaving:
        K'o-ssu." *Hali* 5, no. 1 (1982), pp. 36–42.

Wang
1991   Wang Shifu. *The Moon and the Zither: The*
        Story of the Western Wing. Edited and
        translated with an introduction by
        Stephen H. West and Wilt L. Idema; with a
        study of its woodblock illustrations by
        Yao Dajuin. Berkeley, 1991.

Wang
1986   Wang Shixiang. *Classic Chinese Furniture:*
        Ming and Early Qing Dynasties. Trans.
        Sarah Handler and the author.
        Hong Kong, 1986.

Wang
1990   Wang Shixiang. *Connoisseurship of Chinese*
        Furniture: Ming and Early Qing Dynasties.
        2 vols. Trans. Wang Shixiang,
        Lark E. Mason Jr., et al. Chicago, 1990.

Wang
1995   Wang Yarong. "Embroidery in Ancient
        Chinese Costume." Trans. Don J. Cohn.
        In Urban Council, Hong Kong, and the
        Oriental Ceramic Society of Hong Kong in
        association with the Liaoning Provincial
        Museum. *Jinxiu luoyi qiao tiangong /*
        Heavens' Embroidered Cloths: One-Thousand
        Years of Chinese Textiles. Exh. cat.,
        Hong Kong Museum of Art. Hong Kong, 1995,
        pp. 56–62. [In Chinese and English]

Wang
1999   Wang Liying, ed. *Wucai, doucai* [Five-color,
        Dovetailed-color Porcelains]. *Gugong*
        bowuyuan cang wenwu zhenpin quanji
        [A Compendium of Treasured Antiquities in
        the Collection of the Palace Museum, Beijing]
        series, vol. 38. Ed. Yang Xin.
        Hong Kong, 1999. [In Chinese]

Wang Zhongshu
1982   Wang Zhongshu. *Han Civilization.*
        New Haven, 1982.

Wardwell
1992   Anne E. Wardwell. "Two Silk and Gold
        Textiles of the Early Mongol Period." *The*
        Bulletin of The Cleveland Museum of Art
        79, no. 10 (1992), pp. 354–378.

Wardwell
1992–3 Anne E. Wardwell. "Important Asian Textiles
        Recently Acquired by The Cleveland Museum
        of Art." *Oriental Art* 38, no. 4
        (Winter 1992–93), pp. 244–251.

Wardwell
1994   Anne E. Wardwell. "Gilded *Kesi* Boots of the
        Liao Dynasty (A. D. 907–1125)." *Bulletin*
        du Centre International d'Études des Textiles
        Anciens 2 (1994), pp. 6–12.

Watt et al.
1990   James C.Y. Watt et al. "Recent Acquisitions:
        A Selection, 1989–1990—Asian Art."
        Metropolitan Museum of Art Bulletin 48,
        no. 2 (Fall 1990), pp. 84–95 .

Wilkinson
1998   Endymion Wilkinson. *Chinese History:*
        A Manual. Cambridge, Massachusetts, 1998.

160 **Wilson**
1993　Verity Wilson. "The Far East: China."
Chapter 14 in Jennifer Harris, ed. *Textiles,
5,000 Years: An International History and
Illustrated Survey*. London and New York,
1993, pp. 133–141.

Wilson
1995　Verity Wilson. "Cosmic Raiment: Daoist
Traditions of Liturgical Clothing."
Orientations 26, no. 5 (May 1995),
pp. 42–49. Reprinted in **Orientations 1998**,
pp. 138–145.

Wilson and Thomas
1986　Verity Wilson and Ian Thomas.
Chinese Dress. London, 1986.

Wingate
1984　Isabel Wingate. *Fairchild's Dictionary of
Textiles*. 6th ed. New York, 1984.

Yang et al.
1983　Yang Renkai et al. *Ryōneishō hakubutsukan
zō kakushi shishū / Liaoning sheng
bowuguan cang kesi zixiu* / Tapestry
and Embroidery in the Collection of the
Museum of Liaoning Province. Series 1,
vol. 3. Tokyo, 1983.
[In Japanese, Chinese, and English]

Yang Xin
1988　Yang Xin, Li Yihua and Xu Naixiang.
The Art of the Dragon. Boston, 1988.

Yao
1991　Yao Dajuin. "The Pleasure of Reading
Drama: Illustrations to the Hongzhi Edition
of the Story of the Western Wing," in
*The Moon and the Zither: The Story of the
Western Wing*. Edited and translated with an
introduction by Stephen H. West and Wilt L.
Idema. Berkeley, 1991.

Zhang County Culture Center
1982　Zhang xian wenwuguan [Zhang County
Culture Center]. "Gansu Zhang xian Yuandai
Wang Shixian jiazu muzang: Jianbao zhi er"
[The Yuan-dynasty Tomb of the Wang
Shixian Family in Zhang County, Gansu
province: Second brief report]. *Wenwu* 2
(1982), pp. 13–21 and n.p., pls. 1–2.
[In Chinese]

Zhao
1992 a　Zhao Feng. *Sichou yishu shi* [A History of
Silk Art]. Hangzhou, 1992. [In Chinese]

Zhao
1992 b　Zhao Feng. *Tangdai sichou yu sichou zhi lu*
[The Silks of the Tang Period and the Silk
Route]. In *Sui Tang lishi wenhua congshu*
[Compiled Writings on the History and
Culture of the Sui and Tang dynasties].
Xi'an, 1992. [In Chinese]

Zhao
1999　Zhao Feng. *Zhixiu zhenpin: Tushuo Zhongguo
sizhou yishu shi / Treasures in Silk:
An Illustrated History of Chinese Textiles*.
Hong Kong, 1999. [In Chinese and English]

Zhao
2000　Feng Zhao. "The Chronological Development
of Needlelooping Embroidery." *Orientations*
31, no. 2 (February 2000), pp. 44–53.

Zhou
1987　Zhou Lili. "Ciai bajixiangwen xintan" [New
Light on the *Bajixiang* Motif in Chinese
Ceramics]. *Shanghai bowuguan jikan*
[Bulletin of the Shanghai Museum] 4 (1987),
pp. 312–332. [In Chinese]

Zhu
1962　Zhu Qiqin. *Sixiu biji* [Notes on silks and
embroideries]. In *Xiupu* [Manual on
Embroideries]. In *Yishu congbian* [Collected
writings on art], vol. 1, no. 32 (1962).
[In Chinese]

Zhu
1990　Zhu Qixin. "Royal Costumes of the Jin
Dynasty." *Orientations* 21, no. 12
(December 1990), pp. 59–64. Reprinted in
Orientations 1998, pp. 105–110.

Zurich
1994　Albert Lutz, Helmut Brinker, François Louis,
et al. *Chinesisches Gold und Silber: Die
Sammlung Pierre Uldry* [Chinese Gold and
Silver: the Collection of Pierre Uldry]. Exh.
cat., Museum Rietberg. Zürich, 1994.
[In German]

ISBN 0-910407-39-8

9 780910 407397